Understanding the Environmental Impacts of
Offshore Windfarms

Edited by
Joyce Huddleston

COWRIE

Citation

For bibliographic purposes, this book should be referred to as: Huddleston, J. (ed) *Understanding the environmental impacts of offshore windfarms.* COWRIE.

First published 2010

British-Library-in-Publication Data
A catalogue record for this book is available from the British Library

ISBN: 978-0-9565843-8-0

Designed for COWRIE by NatureBureau Ltd, 36 Kingfisher Court, Hambridge Road, Newbury, Berkshire RG14 5SJ. www.naturebureau.co.uk

Published by COWRIE
Registered Charity No. 1112518

Printed by Information Press, Oxford

Contents

Acknowledgements

This book would not have been possible without the input of a large number of people who put considerable time and energy into its creation on behalf of COWRIE Limited. Our particular thanks go to the authors and their organisations who donated time and knowledge as well as images: Sophy Allen (JNCC); Bill Cooper (ABPmer); Zoe Crutchfield (Mainstream Renewable Power); Carolyn Heeps (Fred Olsen Renewables); Chris Hill (GeoData Institute); Rowena Langston (The RSPB); Eleanor Partridge (NatureBureau); Christopher Pater (English Heritage); Frank Thomsen (Cefas); and Gero Vella (RES Offshore).

Thanks must also go to the COWRIE Board of Trustees for their backing and helpful comments during the book's preparation and in particular, Alan Moore (Chairman) for providing the foreword and Dr Carolyn Heeps (Company Secretary) for her overall leadership of the project. We are also indebted to The Crown Estate for their continued support of COWRIE's work. Among the production team we especially thank Joyce Huddleston (technical writer and editor), Philip Ward (The Leadout Project), Brigitte Ruiz and Eleanor Partridge (project managers for the book at NatureBureau) and Barbara Creed (senior designer at NatureBureau).

Finally we are grateful to all those who donated images for use in the book: ABP Marine Environmental Research Ltd; BioConsult SH GmbH & Co.KG; BWEA (now RenewableUK); Cefas; Centrica Energy; Clipper Wind; CMACS Ltd; The Crown Estate; DONG Energy Power; ECON Ltd; EMU Ltd; English Heritage; GeoData Institute; Giles Aviation Ltd; Green Energy Awards 2009; HiDef Aerial Surveying Limited; JNCC; LaTene Maps; The Leadout Project; Lighthouse Field Station, University of Aberdeen; Mainstream Renewable Power (UK); Marine Biological Association; MarLIN; National Monument Record; NatureBureau Ltd; RES Offshore; The Royal Society for the Protection of Birds (RSPB); RWE npower renewables; Scottish Renewables; Sea Mammal Research Unit, University of St Andrews; SeaMarco; Subacoustech Environmental Ltd; University of Aberdeen; University of St Andrews; Vattenfall; Walney Offshore Windfarms Ltd; Wessex Archaeology Ltd; and The Wildfowl & Wetlands Trust (WWT).

Foreword

In December 2000 the UK's first offshore windfarm was opened and since those first two turbines were installed we have come a long way and learned many things as an industry. COWRIE has been an integral part of the shared learning since its formation in 2005 when we set our charitable objectives *'to advance and improve understanding and knowledge of the potential environmental impacts and benefits of offshore windfarm development in UK waters'*.

This book is both a record of the achievements of COWRIE and a celebration of the co-operation across the UK renewables industry in the learning process.

COWRIE has provided a unique opportunity for industry, regulators, government, nature conservation advisors and NGOs to come together in a forum to achieve consensus on the questions that could be addressed through focused environmental research.

It has worked in collaboration with many different organisations, helping to bring together stakeholders and interest groups to discuss issues and explore practical solutions and mitigation measures. Drawing on the best experts in their fields it has delivered results that have been peer reviewed and are driving forward industry best practice. Consequently, COWRIE has gained an enviable international reputation.

It has achieved its charitable objectives through the dissemination of its work in many different formats including technical reports and studies for specialist use, teaching resources that can be used in schools, and materials and events that are of more general public interest.

The quality of COWRIE's work reflects the contributions of a large number of people in the various working groups, the Secretariat and Board of Trustees, and I'd like to personally thank all of them for their painstaking and professional work. Over 50 reports have been completed on behalf of COWRIE by a range of organisations and individuals. All of those people have seen the value of contributing to COWRIE's work and we are immensely grateful to them.

COWRIE has undoubtedly made a difference, and we could ask no more than that!

Alan Moore OBE, COWRIE Chairman

COWRIE Board of Trustees

Authors

Dr Sophy Allen is Marine Renewables Ornithologist with the Joint Nature Conservation Committee (JNCC) where she is a member of its Marine Advice Team providing specialist policy, guidance and scientific advice on ornithology arising from marine renewable developments and, in particular, offshore wind. Sophy has been involved in avian research and conservation for 10 years and has worked on both threatened and common bird species in marine and terrestrial habitats. For her PhD in New Zealand (University of Canterbury, Christchurch) she investigated the population ecology of introduced bird species. Sophy has practical experience in molecular, behavioural and population level research, and has a Masters in instrumentation, focusing on avian passive telemetry.

Bill Cooper is Managing Director of ABPmer – one of the UK's leading marine environmental consultancies. Bill has been a member of the COWRIE Data Technical Working Group and continues to contribute to the UK Offshore Renewables Energy Environmental Forum and the Ad Hoc Working Group on marine renewable standards. Bill is an oceanographer with over 20 years of practical experience and has supervised coastal process studies for many of the UK's offshore wind projects.

Zoe Crutchfield joined Mainstream Renewable Power in 2009 as Offshore Environment Manager. This role involves managing the environmental impact assessment (EIA) processes for all its offshore developments in the UK starting with Neart na Gaoithe windfarm in Scottish territorial waters. Zoe spent the previous eight years at the Joint Nature Conservation Committee (JNCC) as its Senior Offshore Advisor working with the offshore industries (oil and gas, shipping, aggregates and renewable energy) to reduce the impact of their activities on the marine environment. Zoe has extensive experience in both EIA and the workings of UK government. She was a member of the COWRIE Environment Technical Working Group, and has been a member of steering groups such as Offshore SEA and European initiatives such as OSPAR. Zoe is now actively involved in the work of RenewableUK's Consents and Licensing Group and associated sub-groups.

Dr Carolyn Heeps is a Trustee and Company Secretary for COWRIE Limited. She has been a key figure in the establishment and management of the COWRIE initiative since it began in 2001. At that time she was the Head of Marine Policy and Sustainable Development at The Crown Estate and was responsible for the Round 1 offshore windfarm programme. She helped take COWRIE through to company and charitable status while managing the Round 2 offshore windfarm programme. Carolyn has played a very active role in COWRIE through her involvement in its various working groups and in overseeing the management of the secretariat (NatureBureau Ltd), data management activities (Geodata) and website development (e-bloc). In July 2009 Carolyn joined Fred Olsen Renewables Ltd as Offshore Projects Manager where she is responsible for an expanding portfolio of offshore wind and other marine renewable energy projects.

Chris Hill is Director of the GeoData Institute, an environmental research and consultancy group at the University of Southampton specialising in applied environmental science, data management, processing and analysis. His work includes management of real-time offshore data and webGIS applications for offshore aggregates, regional environmental characterisation and offshore renewables. He has advised on data management plans for offshore developers, processing and analysis procedures for Round 3 site selection, and array planning. He is working with MEDIN (Marine Environment Data and Information Network) on data access policy, interoperability and data stewardship issues across the Marine and Coastal Data Archive Centres. As COWRIE Data Manager, Chris worked on developing its Route Map to Data and supporting the transition of the COWRIE Data Management System to The Crown Estate. Chris was a member of the COWRIE Environment Technical Working Group, the Data Technical Working Group and the Futures Working Group.

Dr Rowena Langston is Principal Conservation Scientist with The Royal Society for the Protection of Birds (RSPB) and has worked in the field of conservation science for over 20 years, mainly with the RSPB and the British Trust for Ornithology (BTO). Her PhD at the University of Durham in shorebird ecology was followed by work on a variety of avian monitoring and surveillance programmes. Her present work combines research and the provision of scientific advice to colleagues in RSPB, BirdLife Partners and other organisations in the UK and abroad. Studying the effects of renewable energy on birds is a major area of work, notably the development of guidance for assessment, monitoring and research. Rowena was a member of the COWRIE Environment Technical Working Group and the Birds Subgroup from their inception.

Christopher Pater is the Marine Planner at English Heritage, a post created in 2005 (he was the first person to hold the role), working as part of its Maritime Archaeology Team. Christopher deals with strategic matters to promote the inclusion of cultural heritage in government activities and responsibilities affecting the marine historic environment with particular reference to the Marine and Coastal Access Act 2009. He also provides advice about specific marine development proposals such as offshore windfarms and port development. Christopher was a member of the COWRIE Environmental Technical Working Group. He was a member of the steering group for two published guidance documents on protecting the marine historic environment and helped to oversee a third project on optimising geotechnical survey techniques to support analysis of the submerged and buried prehistoric environment.

Eleanor Partridge is Marine Project Officer at the environmental consultancy, NatureBureau Ltd, where she provides secretariat services (including project management) to COWRIE and consultancy services in the field of marine conservation. Eleanor worked previously as a consultant to Greenpeace and WWF. She has an MSc in Marine Environmental Management from the University of York where her research focused on the history of exploitation of marine ecosystems.

Frank Thomsen is a Team Leader and Scientific Programme Manager within the Environment and Ecosystem Division at the Centre for Environment, Fisheries & Aquaculture Science (Cefas). He mentors a team of seven scientists and manages a variety of projects dealing with human impacts on the marine environment. He has extensive experience in conducting marine acoustics research, in advising regulatory bodies such as Defra, DECC and the German Federal Maritime and Hydrographic Agency (BSH), and in providing scientific evidence for marine policy bodies such as the OSPAR Commission, the London Convention and the International Council for the Exploration of the Sea (ICES). His areas of expertise are environmental risk assessments, acoustic communication in whales and dolphins, the distribution and abundance of cetaceans, visual and acoustic marine mammal surveys, and the effects of underwater noise on marine mammals and fish.

Gero Vella is a Project Development Manager at RES Offshore assisting Centrica in its development of the Round 3 Irish Sea zone. Gero joined RES in 2003 as Environmental Consents Manager for the team managing the environmental impact assessments for the Inner Dowsing and Lincs offshore windfarm projects. Before joining RES Gero worked as an environmental consultant and has more than 10 years' experience managing marine consents. He has been involved in over 12 offshore windfarm projects and has written a number of papers and research reports on the environmental aspects of offshore windfarm development. Gero is a member of RenewableUK's Consents and Licensing Group, and is an industry representative on the UK Fishing Liaison with Offshore Wind and Wet Renewables Group (FLOWW). He was a member of the COWRIE Environment Technical Working Group, in particular managing a number of the 'fish and benthos' projects.

Joyce Huddleston (editor) is a technical writer and editor specialising in environmental and energy issues. She has worked primarily on publications for Government-funded bodies and programmes including the Office for National Statistics, Environment Agency, Scottish Environment Protection Agency (SEPA), Waste & Resources Action Programme (WRAP), Technology Strategy Board, Envirowise and the Carbon Trust, but also for mainstream publishers such as the Royal Society of Chemistry and Oxford University Press. Her skills were honed producing abstracts for two databases – WasteInfo and the Energy Technology Database Exchange (ETDE). Joyce has a degree in chemistry from Nottingham University and, before embarking on a freelance career, worked at the University of Oxford. She is a member of the Society for Editors and Proofreaders (SFEP).

Abbreviations

AC	alternating current
ALSF	Aggregates Levy Sustainability Fund
AMD	acoustic mitigation device
BACI	before and after control impact analysis
BERR	Department for Business, Enterprise and Regulatory Reform
BTO	British Trust for Ornithology
BWEA	British Wind Energy Association [now RenewableUK]
CCW	Countryside Commission for Wales
Cefas	Centre for Environment, Fisheries & Aquaculture Sciences
CEH	Centre for Ecology and Hydrology
CIA	cumulative impact assessment
CMCS	Centre for Marine and Coastal Studies
CMS	Coastal Management for Sustainability
COWRIE	Collaborative Offshore Wind Research Into the Environment
DAASH	Data Archive for Species and Seabed Habitats
DAC	data archive centre
dB	decibel
DC	direct current
DECC	Department of Energy and Climate Change
Defra	Department for Food, Environment and Rural Affairs
DTI	Department of Trade and Industry
DTWG	Data Technical Working Group [COWRIE]
ECWG	Education and Communications Working Group [COWRIE]
ETWG	Environment Technical Working Group [COWRIE]
EIA	environmental impact assessment
EMF	electromagnetic field
FEPA	Food and Environment Protection Act
GIS	geographical information system

GLS	global location sensing
GPS	global positioning system
HD	high definition
HVDC	high voltage direct current
IKSDI	UK Spatial Data Infrastructure
INSPIRE	Infrastructure for Spatial Information in Europe [Directive]
JNAPC	Joint Nautical Archaeology Policy Committee
JNCC	Joint Nature Conservation Commission
MarLIN	The Marine Life Information Network
MaRS	Marine Resource System
MBA	Marine Biological Association
MEDIN	Marine Environmental Data and Information Network
MFA	Marine and Fisheries Agency
MMO	Marine Management Organisation
MSDI	Marine Spatial Data Infrastructure
NERI	National Environmental Research Institute [Denmark]
NGO	non-government organisation
nm	nautical mile
POD	automated porpoise detector
PVA	population viability analysis
RAG	Research Advisory Group
re 1 µPa	relative to 1 micropascal
RIB	rigid-hulled inflatable boat
RSPB	The Royal Society for the Protection of Birds
SAC	Special Area of Conservation
SEA	Strategic Environmental Assessment
SNH	Scottish Natural Heritage
SPA	Special Protection Area
SPL	sound pressure level
TADS	thermal animal detection system
UKLP	UK Location Programme
WWT	The Wildfowl and Wetlands Trust
ZAP	Zonal Appraisal and Planning

1 An introduction to COWRIE

Dr Carolyn Heeps

COWRIE was set up by The Crown Estate as an independent body to carry out research into the impact of offshore windfarm development on the environment and wildlife, evolving into a charity which has gained global recognition for its scientific and educational work

TODAY, with almost 1 GW of installed capacity, the UK leads the world in the generation of electricity from offshore windfarms. Yet it was only in December 2000 that the UK's first offshore windfarm was opened. This 2 x 2 MW turbine project (see photo), just half a kilometre off Blyth Harbour on the Northumberland coast, set the scene for offshore wind to play a major role in ensuring the UK's energy security and in meeting the Government's challenging climate change goals. Blyth established a new marine industrial sector that will see continued growth and significant expansion throughout UK waters over the next decade.

Due to the significant interest in the Blyth project, The Crown Estate (www.thecrownestate. co.uk) as owner of almost all the seabed around the UK out to the limit of territorial waters (12 nautical miles), launched a competition for a round of demonstration-scale offshore windfarm projects. Potential developers were requested to submit bids for areas of seabed they considered most suited for the construction and operation of offshore windfarms. These projects were limited to areas of 10 km² in territorial waters and a maximum of 30 turbines to generate a minimum installed capacity of 20 MW. The programme was designed to enable this fledgling industry to build projects and to develop the appropriate technical, environmental and financial expertise to construct larger projects in the future. In April 2001, 18 companies were successful in securing potential development sites and 11 projects (now known as Round 1) have so far become operational[1].

1 A total of 13 offshore windfarms were operational in UK waters as of September 2010. For the latest information please see the list on the RenewableUK website (www.bwea.com/ukwed/offshore.asp).

Blyth – the UK's first offshore windfarm. © English Heritage

Round 1 windfarm programme provides opportunity to develop experience

Developers chose their sites for Round 1 according to a range of factors including water depth, availability of a good wind resource, and location off coastal areas offering a good grid connection. Recognising that very little was known at that time about the potential environmental impact of offshore windfarms, they avoided areas of high nature conservation value and heavy usage by other marine activities.

Technological limitations at that time meant that all the Round 1 projects are in water depths of less than 20 metres. At this depth monopile foundations are typically used. It is now possible to build structures in deeper water and using a variety of foundation types. But the costs of installation offshore are much higher than onshore, so it is becoming increasingly necessary to build bigger turbines and these present new technological challenges.

COWRIE is set up

All types of development will have some impact on the marine environment, though this can be both positive and negative. Even though offshore wind is a renewable, clean resource and does not produce carbon emissions, building a windfarm will inevitably have some impact which needs to be assessed. At this early stage in the industry very little was known about the potential environmental impact of offshore windfarms so, in February 2001, The Crown Estate set up a fund to start a research programme. The fund was based on the interest from the refundable deposits paid by the Round 1 developers. The Crown Estate set up a working group of specialist expertise to identify the research priorities and to suggest appropriate allocation of the fund. The group was chaired by The Crown Estate, which also provided administrative support.

The working group (see Annex 1 for a complete list of participants) was made up of representatives of those organisations with a direct interest in offshore windfarm development and was drawn from:

- relevant Government departments – at that time the Department of Trade and Industry (DTI) was the electricity regulator and the Department for Food, Environment and Rural Affairs (Defra) was responsible for conservation input and related environmental consents;
- Government conservation advisors – English Nature (now Natural England), Countryside Commission for Wales (CCW), Scottish Natural Heritage (SNH), Centre for Environment, Fisheries & Aquaculture Sciences (Cefas), Joint Nature Conservation Commission (JNCC);
- The Royal Society for the Protection of Birds (RSPB), a key non-governmental organisation (NGO);
- British Wind Energy Association (BWEA), the main trade association for the renewables industry and now RenewableUK;
- representatives of companies in the wind industry wishing to develop the Round 1 sites.

This group, with its broad range of specialist expertise, was named Collaborative Offshore Wind Research Into the Environment (COWRIE) in recognition of the unique way in which it brought together the players and the offshore windfarm industry.

COWRIE research programme

With a limited amount of money COWRIE set about identifying areas of research for funding. COWRIE's main purpose was to carry out relevant research into the issues that we knew least about and which could answer general questions applicable to all potential windfarm developments. The projects aimed to help fill gaps in our knowledge and identify potential guidance or mitigation measures to ensure that windfarm development was carried out in a sustainable way.

COWRIE's work was not intended to replace any requirements on developers to carry out surveys and studies as part of site-based environmental impact assessments. Instead it was hoped that it would help:

- developers to produce environmental statements based on sound scientific evidence;
- the regulator, relevant Government departments and their advisors gain a better understanding of the potential impacts for planning and consenting purposes.

Early on it was agreed that the priority areas of research related to the potential impact on birds, marine mammals and fish. There was significant interest in three areas.

- The development of appropriate bird survey techniques at sea would help to establish population numbers and to assess the potential displacement of birds from areas of proposed development.
- The widespread use of monopile foundations is known to produce underwater noise during the construction phase (and to a limited extent during operation). Underwater noise can be a particular problem for marine mammals such as whales, dolphins and seals, as well as some fish.
- The individual turbines in an offshore windfarm are connected by inter-array cables and export cables to the shore where they connect to the onshore grid. From an environmental perspective there is concern

There is some concern that electromagnetic fields generated by the cables can affect fish species (e.g. sharks, skates and rays) that are especially sensitive to these fields. © Keith Hiscock

that the electromagnetic fields (EMF) generated by the cables can affect fish species (e.g. sharks, skates and rays) that are especially sensitive to these fields.

It was agreed that all outputs from the COWRIE research programme would be made available to the public. This would primarily be via a dedicated website, though some documents would also be printed for distribution.

Round 2 windfarm programme sets up industry for commercial-scale expansion

Round 1 put down the marker for the establishment of the UK offshore wind industry. No sooner had the developers begun the necessary studies for the statutory environmental impact assessments when the DTI published a consultation paper, *Future Offshore*, in November 2002 setting out the Government's policy and its decision to take a more strategic approach to offshore windfarm development. Subsequently the DTI identified three regions as having the best potential for further development – the Greater Wash, the Thames Estuary and the North West (Liverpool Bay). To comply with the forthcoming Strategic Environmental Assessment Directive, the DTI then undertook a Strategic Environmental Assessment (SEA) of these areas to consider a number of development scenarios to deliver its strategy. These limited the total development possible within the three strategic regions to 4–7.5 GW (including the contribution from Round 1).

The SEA was completed in May 2003 and, following consultation, DTI asked The Crown Estate to make available seabed areas in the strategic regions for further windfarm development. Based on the findings of the SEA and experience from the Round 1 process, DTI issued guidance which included a precautionary

coastal exclusion zone of 8–13 km from the coast to reduce the visual impact of development and to avoid sensitive, shallow-water feeding areas for certain species of sea duck.

In July 2003 The Crown Estate launched a competitive tender process for Round 2 sites. This round was not confined to territorial waters and, in December of that year, The Crown Estate announced 15 successful projects amounting to 7.2 GW, and including sites within and beyond territorial waters. These projects were far bigger than those being developed under Round 1, with some such as the London Array being a proposed 1 GW in size. The locations of Round 1 and 2 sites are shown in Figure 1.1.

COWRIE Limited established to support Round 2

Successful Round 2 developers were required by The Crown Estate to pay a one-off fee called an Option Fee (the amount depended on the scale of the development). These Option Fees were used to boost COWRIE, providing a fund of around £3 million. It was decided that COWRIE should become completely independent, and it was registered as a company in June 2005 and granted charitable status in December 2005. A Board was appointed made up of senior experts with specialist knowledge and experience within the industry, including representatives from The Crown Estate (Board members are listed in Annex 2). The Board had full responsibility for governance of COWRIE Limited as a company and a charity. Auditors and an accountant were also appointed.

In terms of its charitable objectives COWRIE Limited had a very clear aim:

'to advance and improve understanding and knowledge of the potential environmental impacts and benefits of offshore windfarm development in UK waters'.

Figure 1.1 2010 offshore renewable activities.

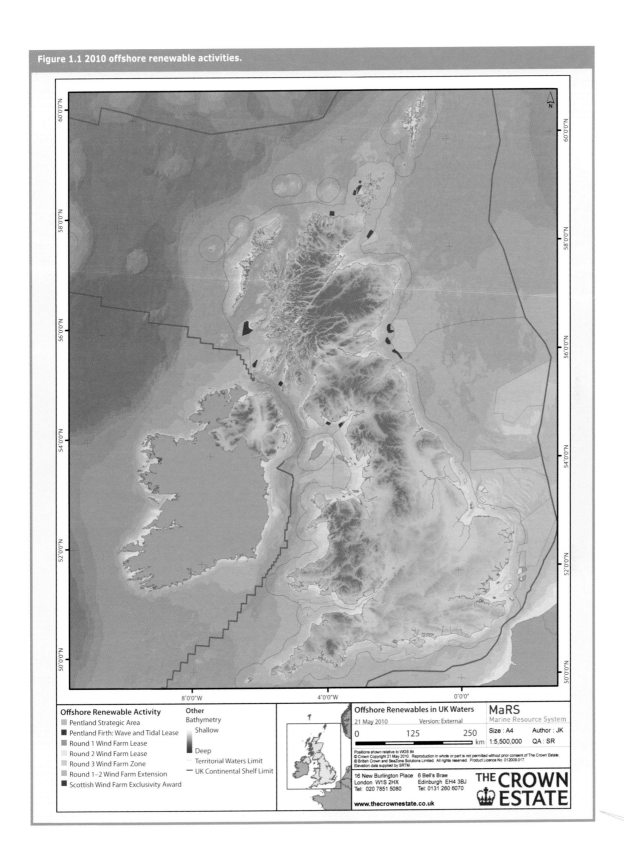

Offshore Renewable Activity
Pentland Strategic Area
Pentland Firth: Wave and Tidal Lease
Round 1 Wind Farm Lease
Round 2 Wind Farm Lease
Round 3 Wind Farm Zone
Round 1–2 Wind Farm Extension
Scottish Wind Farm Exclusivity Award

Other
Bathymetry
Shallow

Deep
Territorial Waters Limit
UK Continental Shelf Limit

Offshore Renewables in UK Waters
21 May 2010   Version: External

0   125   250
km   1:5,500,000

MaRS
Marine Resource System

Size : A4   Author : JK
1:5,500,000   QA : SR

Positions shown relative to WGS 84
© Crown Copyright 21 May 2010. Reproduction in whole or part is not permitted without prior consent of The Crown Estate.
© British Crown and SeaZone Solutions Limited. All rights reserved. Product Licence No. 012009.017.
Elevation data supplied by SRTM.

16 New Burlington Place   6 Bell's Brae
London W1S 2HX   Edinburgh EH4 3BJ
Tel: 020 7851 5080   Tel: 0131 260 6070

www.thecrownestate.co.uk

THE CROWN ESTATE

This aim has been achieved through:

- a coherent programme of short to medium term environmental research leading to the publication and dissemination of reports, guidance notes and best practice documents;
- the management and dissemination of environmental data and information collected, analysed and interpreted throughout the whole life cycle of each windfarm project (from development through operation and decommissioning);
- raising awareness of the UK offshore windfarm programme through a comprehensive education, communications and outreach strategy.

These objectives expanded COWRIE's early remit and were taken forward by three Technical Working Groups representing the main areas of COWRIE Limited's work:

- Environment Technical Working Group (ETWG) – continuing the generic environmental research started during COWRIE's first phase (COWRIE 1);
- Data Technical Working Group (DTWG) – including archiving and dissemination;
- Education and Communications Working Group (ECWG).

The Technical Working Groups consisted of invited experts and representatives from windfarm developers. A considerable number of experts became actively involved in the work of each group, which was chaired by a Board member or trustee who reported back to the Board.

With the significant expansion of the programme, the Board decided to appoint a secretariat to manage the projects and working groups. Following a competitive tender exercise, NatureBureau Limited was appointed as COWRIE secretariat in June 2005.

Expansion and global recognition

COWRIE had thus expanded its remit to include environmental research in its widest sense, while the education and communication objective provided an opportunity to become involved with a broad range of interested stakeholders and marine users, and to develop the COWRIE website into an authoritative source of resources. To fulfil the key charitable objective of public dissemination of COWRIE's work, e-bloc Interactive was awarded the contract to develop the website.

The leasing documents for Round 2 projects included a requirement for developers to submit all their environmental data to The Crown Estate. Management of these data was one of the tasks of the Data Technical Working Group. The work of this group is reported in Chapter 8.

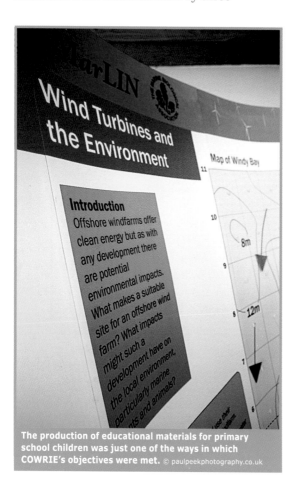

The production of educational materials for primary school children was just one of the ways in which COWRIE's objectives were met. © paulpeekphotography.co.uk

With its publication of peer-reviewed studies, which could be used as guidance and best practice, COWRIE had become recognised beyond the UK for its contribution to furthering our understanding of the key environmental issues associated with offshore wind. The continued active participation of the developer community provided a unique opportunity for the industry to be part of developing its own best practice. Such involvement is crucial to obtaining 'buy-in' of the implementation and delivery of such best practice.

Round 3 and other offshore wind initiatives

In December 2007, while Round 2 projects were being progressed, the Government announced the start of another SEA to consider an additional 25 GW of offshore wind generation from UK waters by 2020. To support the potential significant expansion of the industry, the COWRIE Board felt that another working group should be set up to consider future requirements for environmental research. The Futures Working Group brought together key people from the other groups to establish a programme of studies or surveys that could be delivered in the short term and could make a rapid contribution to support the planned significant expansion to the UK's offshore wind energy programme. A series of key announcements followed.

The Crown Estate identified nine potential development zones for Round 3 (Figure 1.1) and, in June 2008, announced a competitive tender process for the leasing of these large areas which could lead to the development of multiple projects, mainly some distance offshore. This culminated, in January 2009, in the award of nine Zone Development Agreements with a potential 32 GW of capacity, equating to a quarter of the UK's total electricity needs by 2020.

In May 2008 The Crown Estate also announced a competition for projects within Scottish territorial waters. This resulted in the award of 10 sites in February 2009, adding a further 6 GW to UK power generation from offshore wind if all projects are consented.

Driven by developers' appetite, in May 2010 The Crown Estate announced a further 2 GW of potential capacity from five Round 1 and 2 project extensions.

This was followed in August 2010 with The Crown Estate awarding demonstration sites to four companies in response to the need of the UK offshore wind energy industry to demonstrate wind turbines and other technologies. These demonstration sites will help the industry address the technical and cost challenges to install further offshore, as well as providing exciting opportunities for environmental studies and monitoring activities.

As a consequence of this significant expansion of the offshore wind sector, the UK could realise a potential total 48 GW of installed capacity by 2020.

Purpose and structure of this book

This book seeks to provide easy access, in one document, to the main outputs delivered by COWRIE over the past decade. Since its establishment, each COWRIE report has been accompanied by a non-technical summary aimed at the non-specialist reader or for those wanting an overview of each study before reading the full document. COWRIE has not previously attempted to pull together in a single document a synoptic review of all its research output. This book therefore serves a number of purposes.

- It documents the establishment and development of COWRIE, its governance, purpose, objectives and working model. It presents an overview of the entire

COWRIE research programme between 2001 and 2010.

- It categorises the research undertaken into eight themes, summarises the key outputs and main conclusions of each theme, and shows how COWRIE has been successful in reducing the gaps and uncertainties in our environmental knowledge.
- It presents technical information in an easily accessible format enabling readers to gain a rapid understanding of the main issues investigated by COWRIE without having to read the full technical reports archived on the COWRIE website.
- It provides a record of COWRIE's achievements as a legacy to the offshore wind industry.
- It acts as a platform for further research as the industry scales up its programme of development, construction and operation.

In addition to providing a reference for those wishing to learn more about environmental issues, we hope this book will be particularly helpful to new entrants to the industry, government departments, regulators and consultants who wish to gain a rapid understanding of the key environmental issues relating to offshore windfarm development in UK waters.

A thematic approach

In looking again at the programme of research eight themes emerged. Individual members of the working groups with expert knowledge of specific research areas have reviewed relevant reports under each theme. In doing so they have identified the key questions COWRIE investigated and the main conclusions that emerged.

Each chapter of the book relates to a theme, starting at the seabed and working up through the water column and above the sea surface to cover ornithological studies. The ground-breaking work COWRIE has undertaken with

regard to marine data and information is also presented, along with a review of its educational work.

This book, therefore, is arranged under the following themes:

- historic environment;
- coastal processes;
- sound impacts;
- fish and seabed communities;
- marine mammals;
- birds;
- marine data and information;
- education and communications.

Starting at the seabed and sub-sea, COWRIE conducted several studies into marine archaeology under the theme, **Historic Environment**, in recognition that marine archaeology is not just about shipwrecks and associated artefacts, but also about submerged landscapes. The increased survey coverage being carried out by offshore wind developers has provided the marine archaeological community with the fantastic opportunity to collect substantial amounts of new data and information about our marine historic environment in offshore areas.

With shallow water areas close to the shore favoured for development, especially in Round 1, the potential impact on sediment transport pathways resulting in localised scour and changes to coastal processes were considered through a number of studies summarised in the chapter, **Coastal Processes**.

The installation of monopile foundations required for Rounds 1 and 2 of the UK offshore wind programme raised concerns about the potential impacts of pile driving on marine mammals and fish. Consequently, COWRIE conducted research to improve our understanding of the potential impacts and to suggest suitable mitigation measures. The results of this research are presented in the chapter, **Sound Impacts**.

Offshore windfarms require substantial amounts of inter-turbine cabling, as well as export cables to the shore. Recognising that electromagnetic-sensitive species of fish might be affected by the electromagnetic fields from cables, COWRIE has paid significant attention to this challenging issue, providing invaluable new insights and gathering new evidence for behavioural responses. The studies undertaken are described in the chapter, **Fish and Seabed Communities**.

Marine mammals are highly protected species. Recognising the significance of the potential impact of offshore windfarm development, COWRIE facilitated a comprehensive programme of research to consider sound impacts and survey techniques, and undertake a desk-based review of methods of investigating changes in cetacean populations. The results of these studies are presented in a chapter relating to **Marine Mammals**.

The potential of offshore windfarms to impact significantly on bird populations and behaviour requires special attention. COWRIE has made a substantial contribution to these issues, providing a forum for discussion and the exchange of ideas, and publishing numerous reports on windfarm-related bird topics. The results of these studies are presented in the **Birds** chapter.

Perhaps the greatest achievement of COWRIE has been its ability to take an independent view. It has used this position effectively, bringing together regulators, developers, statutory and non-governmental nature conservation bodies to discuss common issues of concern in a professional and non-confrontational environment to agree priority areas of research and ways in which better access to marine data can be guaranteed. The outcome has been successful, resulting in constructive debate, high quality research and best practice guidance for the industry. Recognising the importance of common access to good quality marine data and information, COWRIE has been instrumental in the development of a marine data portal. This is explained in the chapter, **Marine Data and Information**.

Finally, COWRIE's charitable objectives to provide access to all its work are described in the final chapter, **Education and Communications**. Not only has COWRIE provided direct access to its research through publication of the results of all its studies on its website, but it has also recognised the potential to inform future generations of its work through the development and implementation of dedicated resources for schools.

We hope that you find the following chapters informative and interesting, and will visit the website www.offshorewind.co.uk for further information.

2 Historic environment

Christopher Pater

COWRIE guidance has helped raise awareness among offshore windfarm developers of the importance of the historic marine environment, and the need to identify and protect shipwrecks and other seabed archaeological sites within development areas

'THE UNITED KINGDOM'S seas represent a valuable facet of our cultural heritage. There are the thousands of shipwrecks and remains of aircraft that one might immediately think of, but there are also drowned prehistoric landscapes containing artefacts that are more than 8,000 years old.'

Source: *Marine Environment: Sixth Report of Session 2003-2004,* House of Commons Environment, Food and Rural Affairs Committee, 2004

The historic environment is a rich and varied resource. The term 'heritage assets' is used to describe this varied and important legacy and includes buildings, archaeological sites and landscapes of historic interest, whether protected by law or not. Advice to developers, government and the public about the historic environment (from buildings to shipwrecks) in England and the English area of UK territorial waters is provided by English Heritage, and respectively for Wales, Scotland and Northern Ireland by Cadw, Historic Scotland and the Northern Ireland Environment Agency.

As an island nation, the UK has a unique record of maritime activity to and from many countries stretching over millennia. Through use of modern marine survey technologies more and more of this heritage resource is becoming accessible to us.

It is often the case that, due to the depth and water turbidity, divers experience difficulties in physically seeing or filming archaeological sites on the seabed. Now we can use devices such as side-scan sonar and multi-beam sensors to produce instant images of the seabed. It is also possible to use similar surveying technology to that employed by the North Sea oil and gas industry to examine buried and submerged land surfaces and features such as former river systems under the seabed.

Guidance from COWRIE and others

The support of COWRIE has been crucial to the production of guidance that helps to explain how we can look for, interpret and build into the planning of offshore windfarm projects as much knowledge as possible about the historic environment within any area proposed for development. COWRIE has published two such reports:

- *Historic environment guidance for the offshore renewable energy* sector (prepared by Wessex Archaeology, published 2007);
- *Guidance for assessment of cumulative impacts on the historic environment from offshore renewable energy* (prepared by Oxford Archaeology with George Lambrick, published 2008).

A third report, *Offshore Geotechnical Investigations and Historic Environment Analysis: Guidance for the Renewable Energy Sector,* was published in autumn 2010. We hope this last report will be of particular importance to future phases of windfarm development as we have a golden opportunity to develop our archaeological knowledge of a considerable area of what is now seabed (about which we know little), through analysing cores of materiel taken through the seabed to reveal how environmental conditions have changed over thousands of years – between land and sea.

English Heritage and other bodies have an active programme of explaining the importance of the historic environment to offshore developers. Published advice includes:

- *Wind energy and the historic environment* – a position statement by English Heritage published in 2005, which includes consideration of the offshore development and is available from the English Heritage dedicated website, Historic Environment Local Management (www.helm.org.uk);
- *Maritime cultural heritage & seabed development: code of practice for seabed*

development – prepared by the Joint Nautical Archaeology Policy Committee (JNAPC) and published by The Crown Estate in 2006.

The key messages are that:
- all offshore projects should take full account of the historic environment from the earliest stage of planning;
- they should be planned and delivered as effectively as possible incorporating principles of sustainability and without unnecessary impacts on heritage assets.

It is important to recognise the value of archaeological analysis as an integral part of the overall environmental assessment of offshore projects. Professional standards of practice require outputs from archaeological investigations to be published. In this way the results of these archaeological investigations are able to contribute directly to an expansion of our collective knowledge about the marine historic environment.

Offshore windfarms and archaeological investigations

The historic environment – including landscapes of historical, cultural or archaeological significance – is part of the criteria addressed by the environment impact assessment that accompanies every application to build an offshore windfarm. To make such exercises as effective as possible it is important to develop a systematic approach that combines desk-based work checking records and reports with a boat-based marine survey to try to determine what heritage assets may exist in the development area.

Compared with the land, relatively little is known about historic or archaeological sites on the seabed. Across the UK, archives for historic environment information and data are maintained to support management, research and public access. For example, the National Monuments Record for England (maintained by English Heritage) has over 42,500 maritime records which document a multitude of features including prehistoric fish traps exposed at low tide on the coast. Approximately 33,000 of the records refer to shipwrecks. In contrast, there are over a million archaeological sites and find-spots recorded for the land including approximately 18,000 entries on the Schedule of Ancient Monuments (covering about 31,400 sites).

It is common for maritime records to describe an incident such as the reported loss of a vessel on a given date (or thereabouts) and in an approximate location (e.g. vessel foundered 35 miles southeast of Flamborough Head en route from Sunderland). From all these thousands of records we are only aware of approximately 5,200 shipwrecks about which there is confidence about their location on the seabed, but probably not their confirmed identity. The records of losses also predominantly relate to the recording of the shipping market introduced by the establishment of 'Lloyd's List' in 1734.

The actual number of wrecks we can name and have sufficient information to offer an opinion on their archaeological importance is therefore very limited. In addition, very few known sites have the benefit of legal protection – only 60 historic shipwreck sites are designated in the UK territorial sea under the Protection of Wrecks Act 1973.

For example, in England, there are considerable numbers of records of vessels lost in a channel, known as the 'Downs', between the coast and the Goodwin Sands – a short distance offshore from Deal in east Kent and due south of the Thanet offshore windfarm. Three of the historic shipwreck sites designated under the 1973 Act, the Royal Navy warships *Stirling Castle, Northumberland* and *Restoration* were all lost while sheltering in the 'Downs' during the Great Storm of 1703, where it is estimated that as many as 90 vessels may have been lost at this one location. Another victim of this storm was the first Eddystone Lighthouse off the southern Cornish coast.

Other sites at sea are protected because they are the result of armed conflict and are considered 'war graves'. Such sites cover warships and submarines, but also military aircraft. One such site within the proposed Sheringham Shoal offshore windfarm development is HMS *Umpire*, a Royal Navy submarine lost in 1941.

An important point to explain is that much more of the historic environment must be considered than the very few protected historic shipwreck sites. Just because there are no designated sites in an area identified for windfarm development does not mean that similar sites of archaeological and historic importance do not exist there. They may yet be discovered and assessed, and then legally protected if necessary.

Without doubt COWRIE has helped to raise awareness of the historic environment among offshore windfarm developers and to promote an approach summarised in English Heritage's 'Conservation Principles':

- The historic environment is a shared resource.
- Everyone should be able to participate in sustaining the historic environment.
- Understanding the significance of places is vital.
- Significant places should be managed to sustain their values.
- Decisions about change must be reasonable, transparent and consistent.
- Documenting and learning from decisions is essential.

Through effective (i.e. early) project planning informed by COWRIE guidance, it is possible to clarify roles and responsibilities and to plan for appropriate work to be completed prior to development of the windfarm. This may include assessing what documentary evidence is available (e.g. from the respective national archives) and to corroborate that record with geophysical and geotechnical data obtained at sea by the developer. This enables the development of an active partnership between the windfarm developer and national heritage bodies such that the developer produces archaeological information to recognised professional standards during both the environmental impact assessment exercise and subsequent detailed project planning and delivery.

For this process to work effectively, it is important for the national heritage agencies to be involved at an early stage so that surveys are designed to address archaeological requirements such as:

- identifying submerged and buried prehistoric features within the development area;
- confirming the location of features such as shipwrecks, but differentiating them from other natural seabed anomalies.

Thanet offshore windfarm under construction.
© Damian Grady/English Heritage

This approach is best demonstrated by producing archaeological reports that enable mitigation measures to be agreed and put in place as part of an agreed scheme of investigation.

Taking account of how the development may affect seabed archaeological sites is addressed through mitigation and may involve the following:

- The developer produces reports that illustrate and explain sedimentary sequences to reveal new information about previous landscape features.
- The developer agrees that an exclusion zone for all seabed activities will be declared around the site for seabed wrecks and/or other anomalies of archaeological interest.
- A more detailed survey is commissioned to record the site to act as a baseline against which changes can be determined during post-construction monitoring.
- For particular locations, it may be necessary to commission further site interpretation to

assist subsequent management (e.g. the setting of a coastal site of national or international importance may be affected by one or more offshore developments).

New archaeological information

We should not underestimate the importance of the potential of well-planned archaeological studies to reveal substantial new information about the historic environment. Throughout the first two rounds of offshore windfarms developments, good progress has been made in developing standard requirements for how the historic environment should be included in environment impact assessments. We are pleased to see that the industry accepts the completion of projects that take full account of the complex historic environment as good practice.

For example, high resolution marine geophysical surveys carried out as part of

Aerial photo of Thanet offshore windfarm under construction. © Damian Grady/English Heritage

an environmental impact assessment have revealed the presence of sites of potential archaeological interest and the developers were able to avoid them through the declaration of exclusion zones. However, it is crucial that all contractors associated with the project are aware of archaeological matters and it is essential that the overall environmental management plan includes such detail.

It is in our common interest that not only are sites identified to ensure the integrity of, and safeguard, archaeological values, but also to ensure that projects are not delayed due to the sudden and unexpected discovery of important sites. Everyone accepts that an element of risk is involved but, by agreeing an archaeological reporting protocol to be used during construction and subsequent phases, it is possible to put procedures in place so that information can be supplied to archaeologists and decisions about what should be done can be made as quickly as possible. For example, work should immediately move elsewhere so as to

Side-scan sonar image of wreck. © Wessex Archeology

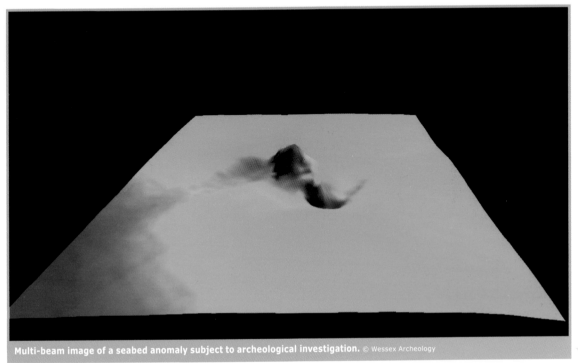

Multi-beam image of a seabed anomaly subject to archeological investigation. © Wessex Archeology

leave any new discovered site as undisturbed as possible while a rapid assessment is undertaken using a variety of techniques (e.g. video or direct diver investigation).

Looking ahead to the assessments necessary to delivery the Round 3 developments, we hope that a substantial amount of information will be produced for a considerable area of seabed. However, the effective gathering of these data is only part of the story and, unless everyone is clear about how information is to be saved, stored and accessed, its full potential will not be realised. In particular, the systematic

investigation of a vast area of seabed (e.g. the southern part of the North Sea) away from regions previously examined by the oil and gas industry and, which has so far received little attention, is expected to produce substantial amounts of new information.

Recent discoveries of Middle Palaeolithic hand axes from 50,000 years ago through the marine aggregates extraction industry in the southern North Sea and publication of *North Sea Prehistory Research and Management Framework* (Peeters *et al.,* 2009) have helped to bring together how the archaeological sector should

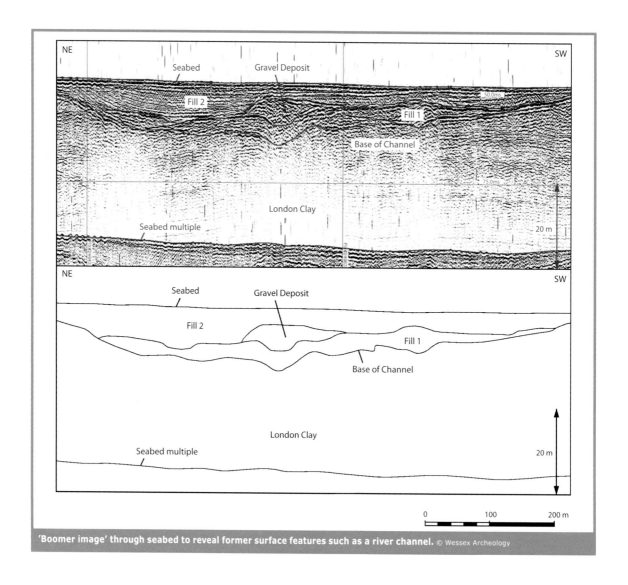

'Boomer image' through seabed to reveal former surface features such as a river channel. © Wessex Archeology

Understanding the Environmental Impacts of Offshore Windfarms

direct activities to expand our knowledge of ancient features preserved within the modern seabed.

In this regard the geotechnical survey guidance produced by COWRIE this year is well-timed. This guidance will supplement work commissioned by English Heritage through the Aggregates Levy Sustainability Fund (ALSF) to examine and optimise how geophysical survey techniques can be used to best effect. Other work supported by ALSF (e.g. on historic seascape characterisation) has a very real application to the planning of the UK's offshore renewable power industry. Such an approach is essential to place in context what records we do have with an appreciation of the many cultural factors that act together to shape the historic character of areas with which we may be unfamiliar and which are very difficult to access. The impetus for this work comes from the Council of Europe European Landscape Convention ratified by the UK Government in 2006.

Lessons learned

There are gaps in our knowledge and the guidance produced by COWRIE will enable this situation to be managed in the future as effectively as possible. English Heritage specifically asked COWRIE to produce guidance that examines complex matters such as cumulative and in combination assessment. We appreciate there are problems in applying such principles to what is a non-quantified resource, but the guidance provides an opportunity for the archaeological community to consider such matters and to assess the implications on the historic environment from a number of perspectives and not just the visual.

The setting of heritage assets is a crucial factor and it is important to consider how this might be affected by offshore development. An example of a particularly sensitive location

is a section of coast close to Heysham in northwest England which contains some of the earliest Christian sites including the nationally and internationally important remains of St Patrick's Chapel, which could date from as early as the 7th century. The approach adopted must be judged according to the location and how changes to the environment such as the construction of offshore windfarms can accommodate historic factors. For a location such as St Patrick's Chapel, it is important to acknowledge that an intrinsic aspect of this site is its immediate proximity to the shoreline and the view over the sea from it. We must then consider how we can reconcile the pressing needs of the 21st century for sustainable power generation with an ancient Christian site and its association with the sea.

Conclusions and the way ahead

We have made good progress in recent years, but there are gaps in our knowledge and a particular area to address is how information is to be archived and made available for the offshore area beyond the remit of the national heritage agencies. It is also apparent that the number of archaeological consultants and contractors is very small and that the sector is working at capacity. Every opportunity must therefore be taken to expand the skills base by ensuring training and education opportunities are available to help deliver these projects.

By placing more information about our shared historic environment in the public realm, we hope it will be possible to be more inclusive in how management is delivered with wider involvement in historic environment decision-making. We will also remain open to identifying and commissioning further guidance as the offshore windfarm industry develops so that the necessary support is available. For example, Round 3 developments will take place further offshore, using new

Rock-cut graves at St Patrick's Chapel, Heysham Head. © Peter Williams/English Heritage

Understanding the Environmental Impacts of Offshore Windfarms

designs in much deeper water. We will continue to support action that contributes to a sustainable future for us all and the discoveries to be made.

References

COWRIE. 2007. *Historic environment guidance for the offshore renewable energy* sector. COWRIE Report ARCH-11-05. Prepared for COWRIE Limited by Wessex Archaeology. COWRIE Limited, London.

COWRIE. 2008. *Guidance for assessment of cumulative impacts on the historic environment from offshore renewable energy.* COWRIE Report CIARCH-11-2006. Prepared for COWRIE Limited by Oxford Archaeology with George Lambrick Archaeology and Heritage. COWRIE Limited, London.

Peeters, H., Murphy, P. and Flemming, N. (ed.). 2009. *North Sea Prehistory Research and Management Framework.* Rijksdienst voor het Cultureel Erfgoed and English Heritage, Amersfoort, The Netherlands, and London, UK.

3 Coastal processes

Bill Cooper

Sediment monitoring and other coastal process studies funded by COWRIE have helped us to understand more about the potential impact on sensitive environmental receptors of large wind turbine arrays, cable laying operations and different types of turbine foundations

COASTAL PROCESS investigations have been undertaken for sites around UK waters for many years. These types of investigations typically consider the physical description of the sea and the seabed, and the potential for any type of development (not just offshore windfarms) to modify these features. The consequences of such modifications may be of direct interest both to project design (i.e. engineering aspects) and to a range of environmental receptors. These receptors may exist across the footprint of the development or be further afield, such as along a nearby coast. An assessment of the sensitivity of the receptors to change in the physical environment is a standard component of an offshore environmental impact assessment (EIA) and follows the widely adopted approach of investigating source–pathway–receptor.

Examples of environmental receptors that could be sensitive to changes in coastal processes include:

- flora and fauna living on and within the seabed;
- historic wrecks and submerged landscapes;
- physical features with nature conservation status such as sub-tidal sandbanks;
- navigation waterways such as channels;
- coastal features such as dunes, salt marshes, beaches and sea defences;
- surfing areas;
- interaction with other developments out at sea such as aggregate industry activities.

Thus coastal process studies can provide vital information to aid the investigation of potential environmental impacts.

Within coastal process studies, the physical description of the sea typically focuses on providing an understanding of the action of the tide and the behaviour of waves, and how these processes might combine to influence the movement of sediments in the water column and on the seabed.

In addition, in some locations the interface between large-scale water bodies can lead to the development of frontal systems which are also commonly associated with areas of high biological productivity. For such locations there may be a requirement to investigate the stability of the front and whether there is any risk of a development interfering with this process.

When applied to a specific project, a coastal processes study needs to cover any physical process that may be relevant to the development – addressing environmental concerns and/or engineering requirements. The scope of the environmental work will typically examine what might be expected to take place in the natural environment over the lifetime of the development to establish an understanding of the baseline and then identify the magnitude, extent and duration of any additional effects which may occur due to the project.

Natural cycles often have a dominant influence, making a good understanding of natural variability essential. Studies need to consider variability due to:

- spring and neap tides;
- seasonal trends in waves;
- longer term effects due to climate change.

Coastal processes and offshore wind

Although the subject of coastal processes is considered a mature area of study, the application of such understanding to offshore wind developments remains relatively new.

Windfarm projects involve placing a large number of turbines out at sea. The turbines are secured to the seabed using appropriate foundations and cables laid to connect them together and to the shore. Understanding what effects this might have on the physical environment requires knowledge of:

- the type, size, number and layout of the structures;
- the methods used to install them;
- how many years the windfarm will operate for.

These effects may occur during the construction phase or develop later during the period of power generation. They may be local to each structure, collectively over the entire footprint of the windfarm or alter environmental conditions further afield. Some effects may be related mainly to environmental interest, others to engineering considerations and some to both.

Since some offshore windfarms may have leases permitting operation for up to 50 years, it is also important to consider what might alter the baseline environmental conditions (i.e. no windfarm development) over the same timescale. For some areas of the seabed, natural variability can be very high and lead to large-scale migration of banks and channels.

Source–pathway–receptor model

While the presence of a structure on the seabed might constitute a direct and localised impact, the structure itself will also alter the local behaviour of waves and tides which in turn may lead to a further impact remote from the structure. A source–pathway–receptor approach is a standard means of considering what environmental risks may occur across the wider area.

A typical application of the source–pathway–receptor model to an offshore wind development includes:

- the foundation structure and support column being considered as the source of a potential effect on the waves or tides;
- the interaction of the waves and tides acting as the pathway for transporting sediment;
- the receptor being a feature identified as being potentially sensitive to any change in sediment movements.

A variety of foundation concepts are currently under consideration in windfarm projects. These range in scale and type from relatively small diameter monopiles to gravity bases with large diameter footprints. There are also jackets and tripods with multiple cross members. The installation methods and considerations for scour protection vary in each case, as do the scale and type of interactions that occur.

A further source of a potential effect is the process of laying the cables required to link up the turbines and to export the electricity produced to shore. Although cables are laid along a fairly confined route, it is necessary to consider the range of soil types into which the cables will be buried and the depth of burial. A variety of tools and methods may be needed to manage these issues and to minimise the disturbance to the seabed.

Across an array of devices, effects could be represented by lots of individual sources with the potential for the interaction between the sources and pathways to become additive. However, the generally small footprint of individual sources and the fact they are separated by relatively large distances tends to reduce the potential for any greater effect occurring over the scale of the full array. Where bigger structures (e.g. gravity bases) are being considered, the interference and spreading effect on the pathways becomes greater and the likelihood of some form of array-scale change increases.

Coping with uncertainty in predictions of potential environmental effects

Before the first projects were constructed, our understanding of the scale and significance of any effects on the marine environment from windfarm developments relied heavily on a hypothesis-based approach. This left high levels of uncertainty when predicting potential environmental effects. These uncertainties were partly addressed by taking the conservative approach of investigating realistic worst-case scenarios and by including a requirement for environmental monitoring in the licence conditions to confirm predictions.

Floating	Jacket	Tripod	Monopile	Bucket	Gravity Base	Sheet Pile
Water depth (m): 30+	Water depth (m): 20-50	Water depth (m): 20-50	Water depth (m): 0-30	Water depth (m): 0-30	Water depth (m): 0-15	Water depth (m): 0-10
Weight (ton): N/A	Weight (ton): N/A	Weight (ton): N/A	Weight (ton): 100-400	Weight (ton): N/A	Weight (ton): 1,000-1,500	Weight (ton): N/A
References: N/A	References: N/A	References: N/A	References: HR 1 HR 2 BURBO GUNFLEET SANDS Q7	References: HORNS REV FREDERIKSHAVN	References: NYSTED LILLEGRUND	References: FREDERIKSHAVN RØNLAND

Range of typically available foundation options and water depths. © Dong Energy Renewables

Although these monitoring programmes involved specific projects, the information obtained from them had wider importance in establishing an overall evidence base for critical review in support of future projects.

Reflections on early projects raised two general questions:

- Just how good are the hypothesis-based predictions?
- What is the current best practice approach to addressing the issues?

UK windfarm developments and coastal processes

Round 1

The offshore windfarms in Round 1 are small-scale developments at dispersed nearshore locations around the coast of England and Wales, with monopiles as the favoured foundation option. The size constraints placed on Round 1 developments were intended to keep the environmental risks to a minimum and to offer a learning opportunity for the fledgling offshore wind industry.

Despite the maturity of coastal process science at this time, the newness of the offshore wind industry brought with it many unknowns. These unknowns heightened some initial concerns as to exactly what type and scale of effects might occur. These issues were investigated through the EIA process and included potential effects on the coast. A typical approach was based on adopting a conservative worst-case scenario to partly address the lack of evidence for actual effects. Various research projects and project-related monitoring programmes were also implemented to address concerns.

Those Round 1 projects that are now operational are producing a range of vital environmental monitoring evidence which covers a number of themes related to coastal processes. The importance of reviewing this information at a generic level to inform later phases of project development was widely

Gradually spreads out and recovers to original speed

Narrow turbulent wake

Flow unaffected here

Flow unaffected here

Flow blocked locally by the foundation

Direction of tidal flow

Scale of interaction of surface flows around monopile foundation. © ABPmer recognised and led to a key project for the industry funded by Government which reviewed the lessons learnt from the Round 1 sediment process monitoring data (DECC, 2008).

Round 2

In Round 2 the projects increased in size by an order of magnitude but were clustered within three strategic areas (underpinned by completion by UK Government of a Strategic Environmental Assessment; see DTI, 2003). Although the distance from the coast also increased (a coastal exclusion zone was set to avoid concerns about effects on the coast and visual impact), and sites were awarded beyond the territorial limit, most projects remained close to shore and across shallow depths. The foundation options being considered also broadened to include a variety of gravity base and multi-pile designs alongside the monopile option. These larger scale projects considering alternative foundation options, and also closer together, introduced a new set of concerns – especially those related to potential cumulative effects. At the time of writing the majority of Round 2 projects are still waiting to be built and so there is no evidence base from these new projects.

Round 3

For Round 3 the scale of development is even more challenging. The Crown Estate has designated nine zones around the UK, targeting an additional installed capacity of 25 GW by 2020. The declaration of the Renewable Energy Zone (REZ) under the Energy Act 2004 has also enabled consideration of development rights across the entire UK Continental Shelf and hence Round 3 zones are not restricted to territorial waters. The spread of locations and scales for zones provides a diverse set of coastal process environments as well as many new technical challenges. In turn, the engineering

solutions required to develop such areas are the subject of further research which seeks to reduce the cost of project delivery.

Coastal process studies today

Over the course of undertaking coastal process studies around the UK, the scale, type and location for offshore windfarm developments has evolved rapidly from round to round. In general, the focus of the corresponding set of environmental concerns has also moved away from potential issues at the coast – though there are still a few projects nearshore and a few where coastal process issues may still be important. It also remains necessary to consider the potential effects of export cables from the windfarm to the shore.

Despite the change of focus to more offshore sites, the topic remains under the familiar name of 'coastal processes' with the specific range of requirements relevant to each project determined on a case-by-case basis.

In response to the evolving industry, the challenges of new locations and a broader range of engineering options has been a corresponding requirement to evolve technical approaches to investigate the range of issues and to collect the necessary data to support such approaches.

COWRIE coastal processes projects

COWRIE has funded two important projects to advance the understanding of coastal processes to offshore wind projects. This work was designed to sit alongside other generic research on this subject, but the emphasis for COWRIE was to carry out work to aid understanding that related only to environmental concerns.

An important element in these projects was to incorporate the views of both the experts involved in developing coastal process studies and those bodies providing independent technical reviews on behalf of regulators. This allowed a consensus approach and common level of understanding to be achieved.

Best practice guide

The first of the two projects came about from the recommendation by the Marine and Fisheries Agency (MFA) representative on the COWRIE Data Technical Working Group to undertake a study to:

- learn more about the range of tools being used to support coastal process studies;
- understand the respective strengths and weaknesses of such tools;
- consider best practice approaches for their application in future projects.

This would help regulatory bodies and others to gain a better understanding of the strength of evidence produced by such tools. This in turn would help when making decisions about consents for future projects and inform the need for any further monitoring requirements.

Previous guidance on coastal processes and offshore wind had looked only at the anticipated requirements from Round 1 offshore windfarms and was thus more aligned to small-scale projects closer to the coast and with monopile foundations. This guidance offered:

- an initial insight into the range of coastal process issues expected to be relevant to projects of this type;
- a description of the main tools available to support investigation of the issues.

The new project updated this guidance and shifted the alignment to potential issues related to Round 3 projects at the same time. The COWRIE best practice guide for coastal process studies sought to anticipate other efforts to update existing EIA guidance in support of Round 3. The aim was to ensure that the more encompassing EIA guidance would marry together with the best practice guide to offer a more specific and detailed advice on the topic of coastal processes.

The updated guidance (Lampkin *et al.*, 2009) recognises a number of key issues for coastal and seabed impact assessments still considered of particular interest in the context of an offshore windfarm EIA (Table 3.1). The guidance also includes suggested approaches for investigating these issues. It pays particular attention to modelling tools and notes the range of applicable uses, the reliability of predictions and potential uncertainties that need to be managed.

Relevance testing is achieved on a case-by-case basis through project scoping as not all issues may be relevant to all sites. In some cases there may also be other exceptional issues (e.g. the proximity of the windfarm development to coastal type fronts) which are only relevant to a single geographic area.

The guidance aims to provide an objective approach to defining the basis for selecting field data collection and/or numerical modelling to support EIA studies. This can be thought of as follows: if the question(s) relating to completion of the EIA is well defined and can be answered on the basis of existing evidence (including existing site data or numerical model results), then the need to obtain new or more detailed data from the field or perform further numerical modelling studies is questionable. Conversely, if the question(s) cannot be answered on this basis then field data collection or numerical modelling can be considered.

Further review of sediment monitoring data

The purpose of the second project was to revisit the earlier study published by DECC in 2008 and to update the evidence base for coastal process issues to bring in further data and information from a broader range of built offshore windfarms (Carroll *et al.*, 2010). This new exercise was timed to be available to support Round 3 requirements and the need for more information to describe the potential effects due to gravity base structures. Importantly, the data gathered by this exercise have also been fed into the COWRIE marine GIS database (see Chapter 8).

The scope of the project was integrated with a separate study, 'Strategic review of offshore windfarm monitoring data associated with FEPA licence conditions' (ME1117) funded by Defra. This study by Cefas is also due to report in 2010 and includes a more general review of all monitoring themes presently required in support of Food and Environment Protection Act (FEPA) licence conditions.

As with the original sediment monitoring project, the range of windfarm sites targeted for review included overseas projects as well as recently completed projects around the UK. Newly commissioned windfarms off the Dutch and Belgium coasts were deliberately targeted, with special attention being given to the Thornton Bank windfarm off the Belgian coast.

Although Round 1 and Round 2 projects have continued to use monopile foundations, it is expected that Round 3 developments will be built using a wider range of foundation types and particularly gravity base foundations. The Thornton Bank windfarm represents a fairly unique example of a gravity base installation across a sandbank environment and in coastal process conditions not dissimilar to some Round 3 sites. Available information from Thornton Bank has been collated into the COWRIE evidence base (monitoring is continuing).

The evidence base now also includes more discussion on the issue of scour and scour protection, along with examples of present best practice. These show that, with good planning and understanding, scour protection can work without creating further effects away from structures.

The COWRIE study has successfully extended the evidence base but there remain critical gaps in understanding which will require future monitoring. It is also crucial to continue to:

- support an evidence-based approach to consenting projects and the monitoring information that needs to be collated;
- maintain the database of evidence – and not just for monitoring related to coastal processes.

This is a key recommendation from the study and an important consideration for any future industry research funds.

Table 3.1 Key issues for offshore windfarm environmental impact assessments.	
Issue	**Relevant to:**
Suspended sediment dispersion and deposition patterns resulting from foundation and cable installation or decommissioning	Receptors sensitive to specific changes in burial depth, suspended sediment loads or textural change in sedimentary habitats
Changes in coastal morphology due to cable landfall installation and maintenance	Receptors sensitive to erosion or accretion including habitat, property, recreation and landscape
Scour and scour protection	Receptors sensitive to the introduction of new substrate
Wave energy dissipation or focusing for sites very close (<5 km) to an exposed shoreline for foundation types and/or array densities considered more likely to affect wave height, period or direction	Receptors sensitive to changes in coastline morphology
Wave and current processes controlling very shallow sandbank morphology, especially for relatively dense turbine arrays and/or less well understood foundation types	Ecological or navigation receptors sensitive to changing bed morphology including scour, channel migration and sandbank mobility

Typical arrangement of present offshore wind turbines – small foundation structures widely spaced. © ABPmer

Understanding the Environmental Impacts of Offshore Windfarms

Conclusions

In general, the hypothesis-based approach used to support early environmental impact assessments has been upheld by the evidence now becoming available from completed windfarm projects.

Impacts to the seabed can be apparently local to areas where devices have been installed and are generally in line with predictions given in the environmental impact assessment.

Some of the most important impacts are local scour around the base of monopile foundations and secondary scour around poorly implemented scour protection.

To date there is no evidence to suggest offshore wind has had any impact on seabed morphology outside of local scour.

For some locations where sediment transport is relatively low, the depressions of jack-up legs remain visible on the seabed. But for areas where sediment transport is high or the seabed conditions are more resistant, these depressions are not visible.

Key gaps in the evidence base relate to the use of other forms of foundation structures and in large arrays (which will be typical of the development within Round 3 zones).

It is hoped that the combination of the best practice guide and continued use of an evidence based approach will provide value to the activities required to support future rounds of large-scale offshore wind development.

References

Carroll, B., Cooper, B., Dewey, N., Whitehead, P., Dolphin, T., Rees, J., Judd, A., Whitehouse, R. and Harris, J. 2010. *A further review of sediment monitoring data.* COWRIE Report ScourSed-09. Report prepared for COWRIE by ABPmer with Cefas and H R Wallingford. COWRIE Limited, London.

DECC. 2008. *Review of Round 1 sediment process monitoring data – lessons learnt.* Department of Energy and Climate Change, London.

DTI, 2003. *Environment Report: offshore wind SEA.* Department of Trade and Industry, London.

Lampkin, D.O., Harris, J.M., Cooper, W.S. and Coates, T. 2009. *Coastal process modelling for offshore wind farm environmental impact assessment: best practice guide.* COWRIE Report COAST-07-08. Report prepared for COWRIE by ABPmer and H R Wallingford. COWRIE Limited, London.

4 Sound impacts

Frank Thomsen

COWRIE research has produced vital information on the sounds emitted during the construction and operation of offshore windfarms, the impact of these sounds on the hearing of marine mammals and fish, and possible measures to mitigate these impacts

WATER IS an ideal medium for sound. Sound underwater travels more than four times faster than in air and absorption is less compared to air (see information box). Vision, touch, smell and taste are limited in range and/or the speed of signal transmission. As a consequence many forms of marine life use sound as their primary mode of communication, to locate a mate, to search for prey, to avoid predators and hazards, and for short- and long-range navigation. Activities generating underwater sound can affect these functions and, since sound can be far ranging, the spatial scale of impacts can be quite large.

The offshore windfarm industry produces sound during all its stages (pre-construction, construction, operation and decommissioning). When COWRIE began in 2001 initial sound measurements at some existing sites in Sweden and Denmark suggested that construction was the noisiest activity and, as such, potentially the most problematic for marine life. However, the data were far from comprehensive and the assessment of the impact of offshore windfarm sound on marine mammals, fish and other organisms was therefore limited.

Before COWRIE was set up, little attention had been paid to the sensitivity of marine life to offshore windfarm sounds and potential impacts with regard to temporal and spatial scales. There were few empirical studies, and measures to mitigate against potentially severe impacts had not been addressed. This chapter provides an overview of COWRIE studies dealing with sound impacts.

Information box: Underwater sound

Sound pressure

Sound in water is a travelling wave in which particles of the medium are alternately forced together and then apart. The sound can be measured as a change in pressure within the medium, which acts in all directions, described as the sound pressure. The unit for pressure is Pascal (Newton per square metre).

Each sound wave has a pressure component (in Pascals) and a particle motion component indicating the displacement (metres), the velocity (metres per second) and the acceleration (metres per second^2) of the molecules in the sound wave. Depending on their receptor mechanisms, marine life is sensitive to either pressure or particle motion or both. The pressure can be measured with a pressure sensitive device such as a hydrophone (an underwater microphone).

Due to the wide range of pressures and intensities and taking the hearing of marine life into account, it is customary to describe these using a logarithmic scale. The most generally used logarithmic scale for describing sound is the decibel scale (dB).

The sound pressure level (SPL) of a sound is given in decibels (dB) by:

$$SPL \text{ (in dB)} = 20 \log_{10} (P/P_0)$$

where P is the measured pressure level and P_0 is the reference pressure. The reference pressure in underwater acoustics is defined as 1 micropascal (µPa). As the dB value is given on a logarithmic scale, doubling the pressure of a sound leads to a 6 dB increase in sound pressure level. As the reference pressure for measurements in air is 20 µPa, and water and air differ acoustically, the dB levels for sound in water and in air cannot be compared directly.

Decibel values can be given in different units. Used here are peak-to-peak (pressure from lowest to highest point of the sound waveform), peak (pressure from zero to highest point of the waveform) and root-mean-square (RMS; root-mean square of time series Pressure (time)). Peak pressures are often used to describe impulsive sounds such as pile driving; RMS values are useful for continuous sounds, e.g. those from drilling.

Particle motion

Most terrestrial animals are sensitive to sound pressure. However, fish and many invertebrates are also sensitive to particle motion. Particle motion sensitivity has been shown to be important for fish responding to sounds from different directions.

Sound or noise?

The terms 'noise' and 'sound' are not clearly distinguished. Commonly 'sound' is a very broad term including all acoustic waves, whereas 'noise' refers to sound that is unwanted. But as we do not really know what marine organisms perceive as 'unwanted', this chapter uses the more neutral term 'sound'. The only exceptions are scientifically established terms such as 'ambient noise' or when reference is made to work using that term.

Sounds produced during windfarm construction and operation

Nedwell and Howell (2004) examined published information on sound measurements during the whole windfarm lifecycle from pre-construction to decommissioning. Pile driving techniques were described in detail including:

- impact pile driving – where a pile is hammered into the ground by a hydraulic ram;
- vibropiling – where rotating eccentric weights create an alternating force on the pile, vibrating it into the ground.

Impact pile driving for large diameter monopiles has been the most commonly used method in offshore windfarm construction. The review indicates that sound during this activity might be of particular concern as calculated source levels are very high, ranging between 192 and 261 dB relative to 1 µPa (re 1 µPa; linear peak levels) at one metre. The study also introduced the first ideas about how an assessment of impacts of sound could be performed.

Subacoustech Ltd (Nedwell et al., 2004, 2007) made detailed measurements of the sounds of construction and operation at five offshore windfarm sites in the UK:

- west coast – North Hoyle, Burbo Bank and Barrow;
- east coast – Scroby Sands and Kentish Flats.

These studies confirmed that pile driving is accompanied by very high source levels of 243–257 dB re 1 µPa (peak-to-peak) at 1 m (average 250 dB re 1 µPa at 1 m).

The pile driving sound also covers a wide range of frequencies and well above 20 kHz (the upper range of hearing in humans), and maxima were in the lower frequency range below 1 kHz.

The pile driving sound could be measured far away from the construction site, with very considerable sound pressure levels of well in excess of 160 dB re 1 µPa (peak-to-peak) at distances of 10 km in some cases.

In contrast the measurements obtained during operation were much lower than during construction, with little turbine sound detectable by a hydrophone at distances beyond the windfarm site.

In another review the German consultants biola (Thomsen et al. 2006) provided construction sound measurements undertaken in German waters by the Institute for Technical and Applied Physics (ITAP), Germany, on jacket pile foundations (four piles with smaller diameters than monopiles). ITAP calculated broadband source sound pressure levels of 228 dB re 1 µPa (peak), which though lower than those calculated from monopiles (see above), were still relatively high.

However source sound pressure levels refer to sound back-calculated to a distance of one metre from measurements farther away. The calculated value depends on the transmission loss formula used, which can differ between investigations. The values are therefore difficult to compare. Thomsen et al., (2006) calculated sound ranges using a transmission loss formula derived from measurements in the German Bight. The loudest frequencies (<1 kHz) had sound pressures of more than 140 dB re 1 µPa (peak) at a range of 80 km from the source, indicating very long ranges over which construction sound could be detected above ambient noise in most circumstances.

In addition to these pioneering reports on offshore windfarm sound, COWRIE also funded Subacoustech Ltd to perform research into sounds emitted during drilling for a tidal turbine in the UK (Nedwell and Brooker 2008). This is a vital issue as there are plans to install wave and tidal generators at a variety of locations around the UK and elsewhere with little information on construction and operational sound profiles and hence potential impacts on marine life.

Pile driving activity on board the HLV Svanen at RWE npower renewables' Rhyl Flats offshore windfarm – one of 25 x 40 m long monopiles which were driven into the seabed off the North Wales coast. © Guy Woodland. Reproduced by kind permission of RWE npower renewables

At distances between 28 m and 2 km, sound levels of 105–139 dB re 1 µPa (RMS; 1 second integration time) were found. From these measurements the back-calculated source level was 162 dB re 1 µPa (RMS; one second integration time) at 1 m. This is within the range of sounds from a small vessel. It was concluded that drilling sounds were much lower than, for example, offshore windfarm construction sound. However, they are louder than the operational sound from marine wind turbines. Based on modelling exercises, the impacts on marine mammals and fish were deemed to be restricted to a range of a few hundred metres at most.

COWRIE has also co-funded benchmark research into the measurement of ambient noise in studies to assess the impacts of seismic surveys on cetaceans (bottlenose dolphins and harbour porpoises) in the Moray Firth. An important task in this investigation is to document the current ambient noise levels in the Moray Firth to provide a baseline for further assessments. The University of Aberdeen, which is leading the study, contracted an acoustic consultant (Kongsberg Maritime Limited) to build a device that could measure ambient noise at a very wide range of frequencies (1 Hz to 150 kHz). The first test made in autumn 2009 showed some very promising results (Thompson *et al.*, 2010).

Effects of sound on marine life

Assessing the impacts of sound on marine life is challenging as there are many uncertainties involved. For example transmission loss – and therefore the range over which sound can have an impact – depends on the wind and weather, sea bottom composition and profile, water depth and many other variables that are highly site specific. Modelling exercises using specific transmission loss formula can therefore provide only a very rough estimate of impact range. On the other hand hearing in marine mammals and fish is very diverse in terms of sensitivity,

frequencies covered and even if pressure or particle motion is the most relevant stimulus (see information box). The COWRIE reports by Subacoustech (Nedwell *et al.*, 2004, 2007) and biola (Thomsen *et al.*, 2006) provide detailed reviews on marine mammal and fish hearing.

Marine mammals

For example, harbour porpoises have a very wide hearing range covering lower frequencies of 250 Hz as well as the ultrasonic range up to 160 kHz and perhaps more. Areas of best hearing are shifted to the higher frequencies above 100 kHz, well in the range of their biosonar which operates around 130 kHz. Yet they can still pick up relatively quiet sounds at and below 1 kHz.

Harbour seals hear very well underwater and exhibit a very wide hearing range as well, with hearing up to the ultrasonic range (>20 kHz). Their sensitivity at lower frequencies is better than that of porpoises (seals communicate underwater through low frequency calls).

These hearing studies provide important starting points for any impact studies, yet only a few individuals have so far been tested and the results indicate a high degree of variability between individuals (Thomsen *et al.*, 2006). More investigations on hearing in porpoises and

Harbour porpoises have a very wide hearing range.
© Ron Kastelein

seals are needed to gain a comprehensive understanding of sound-related impacts.

Fish

Both the Subacoustech (Nedwell *et al.,* 2004) and biola (Thomsen *et al.,* 2006) reviews point out that the hearing diversity between different fish species is even more complex than that of marine mammals as there are different hearing groups based on anatomical features. There are species without a swim bladder (e.g. flatfish) which are only sensitive to particle motion; others (e.g. cod) are sensitive to both pressure and particle motion and exhibit a relatively good sensitivity. Finally there are hearing specialists (e.g. herring) with a very good sensitivity over a comparably wide frequency range.

In general, the hearing range in fish is smaller than in marine mammals and in general shifted to the lower end of the scale from below 50 Hz to 500–1,500 Hz. Only a few species such as herring are able to perceive higher frequencies. This is of particular relevance in impact studies of offshore windfarms as the studies by COWRIE indicate that the most energy during construction and operation is emitted at frequencies below 1 kHz. Yet for fish the same note of caution applies as for marine mammals; from the approximately

Harbour seals hear very well underwater. © Keith Hiscock

29,000 species known, hearing has been tested in only about 100.

Type of effect

The effects of sound on marine life can vary depending on a number of internal and external factors (Thomsen *et al.,* 2006) and can broadly be divided into:
- masking;
- behavioural disturbance;
- hearing loss (temporary or permanent);
- injury.

In extreme cases, and at very high received sound pressure levels that are usually close to the source, very intense sounds might also lead to the death of marine life.

Masking happens when the sound hinders detection of biologically relevant sound signals. Behavioural disturbances are changes in activity in response to a sound and can range from very subtle changes in behaviour to strong avoidance reactions.

In marine mammals and fish, behavioural responses can potentially occur at relatively low levels of noise exposure and therefore impact zones can be quite large. These responses may prevent marine mammals and fish from reaching breeding or spawning sites, finding food, and acoustically locating mates – leading to potential long-term effects on reproduction and population parameters. In fish, for example, avoidance reactions can result in displacement away from potential fishing and spawning grounds resulting in lower catches and reduced reproductive capacity respectively.

Hearing loss goes along with changes in the ability of an animal to hear, usually at a particular frequency, with the difference that temporary hearing loss is recoverable after hours or days and permanent hearing loss is not. Permanent threshold shift is considered to be auditory injury. Finally, injury can affect auditory as well as non-auditory tissues.

Impact modelling

Impact modelling work by Subacoustech (Nedwell *et al.*, 2004, 2007) was based on its measurements at five different construction locations (North Hoyle, Burbo Bank, Barrow, Scroby Sands and Kentish Flats). It involved an assessment based on marine life hearing thresholds at different frequencies on the one hand, and the frequency spectrum of impact pile driving sounds on the other. The results indicate variable avoidance responses in porpoises, seals, cod, herring and flatfish at considerable distances from the construction site (several hundreds of metres to several kilometres depending on species and site). The studies postulate that injuries should only happen at relatively close range to the pile driving operation. However, these theoretical values would need further empirical proof.

In a similar assessment, biola (Thomsen *et al.*, 2006) did estimate detection ranges for impact pile driving (jacket pile constructions, see above) of at least 80 km for harbour porpoises, seals and herring, and perhaps very wide ranges of several kilometres for sole and salmon, which have relatively poor hearing abilities. Yet the biola team were hesitant in providing impact ranges for behavioural reactions based purely on modelling and literature data for other species (Thomsen *et al.*, 2006). Based on empirical studies at offshore windfarm sites in Denmark, they concluded that behavioural reactions in harbour porpoises

Cod showed behavioural responses to pile-driving sounds. © Fiona Crouch, MarLIN

could occur at ranges of 20 km or more. They also concluded that injuries in marine mammals and fish should be restricted to close ranges though these predictions were based mainly on theoretical values.

No thresholds for behavioural response for fish could be given and this was identified as a serious gap in the understanding of the sound-related impacts of offshore windfarms.

First experimental study

The studies by Subacoustech and biola provided important insights into the potential impacts of offshore windfarm sounds on marine mammals and fish. However, empirical studies were limited and uncertainties in these assessments were therefore high. COWRIE yet again took the initiative and in 2008 funded the first experimental study on the effects of pile driving on the behaviour of marine fish anywhere in the world.

The study was carried out by the Centre for Environment, Fisheries & Aquaculture Science (CEFAS) in co-operation with Cranfield University, Cornwall College and the University of Stockholm (Mueller-Blenkle et al., 2010). An underwater speaker was used to play back recordings of pile-driving sound to cod and sole held in two large (40 m) net pens located in a quiet bay in west Scotland. Measuring the received sound pressure and particle motion levels gave an idea of the amount of sound to which the fish were exposed. Acoustic

The acoustic underwater speaker for the COWRIE playback experiments. © M H Anderson

Field scientist Christina Mueller and her acoustic equipment during the COWRIE playback experiments in summer 2009. © M H Anderson

radio tags were attached to fish to allow their movements to be analysed.

At relatively low received sound pressure levels (range: 140–161 dB re 1 µPa (peak)), both cod and sole showed a change in their movement patterns. When the recording was played back to the fish, the swimming speed for sole increased; this fell again once the recording stopped. Cod showed similar patterns although to a lesser extent; they displayed a significant freezing response (swimming speed dropped) when the recording was started. Both species tended to move away from the source of the sound when the recording was played. After hearing the sound several times both species did not react as strongly as they did when it was first heard, suggesting that fish may become accustomed to the sound. Finally, there was a high variation in reaction to sound between individual fish.

This study is the first to document the behavioural response of marine fish due to playback of pile driving sounds. The results indicate that a range of received sound pressure and particle motion levels will trigger behavioural responses in sole and cod. The results further imply a relatively large zone of behavioural response to pile-driving sounds in marine fish. However, the exact nature and extent of the behavioural response require further investigation (e.g. some of the results point toward habituation to the sound).

The results of this first experimental study could have important implications for regulatory advice and the implementation of mitigation measures in the construction of offshore windfarms in the UK and elsewhere. They demonstrate that the concerns raised about the potential effects of pile-driving noise on fish were well founded, suggesting to both regulators and developers that the costs imposed by those mitigation measures which have so far been applied following the precautionary principle go some way to addressing a real problem.

The results of the Cefas study indicated that behavioural thresholds should be considered when assessing the impacts of offshore windfarms in the UK and elsewhere. Mitigation measures should be further discussed, developed and, if meaningful, applied – especially if these could lead to a reduction in the acoustic energy emitted to the water column.

Further studies could investigate the response at critical times (e.g. mating and spawning) and the effects of pile driving on communication behaviour. It will also be necessary to further investigate habituation to the sound to effectively manage the effects of pile-driving sound on marine fish.

Mitigation of impacts

Another focus of COWRIE's research into underwater sound was a review of mitigation measures to reduce sound-related impacts.

Use of acoustic mitigation devices

To start with, COWRIE commissioned SMRU Ltd (a consultancy closely linked to the Sea Mammal Research Unit at the University of St Andrews) to look at the potential of using acoustic mitigation devices (AMDs) (Gordon et al., 2007). AMDs are devices that give out a wide variety of sounds to which marine mammals and fish are adverse. They have been employed in fish farming in the UK and elsewhere to chase away seals and in fisheries to avoid the incidental bycatch of porpoises and other cetaceans.

The SMRU study investigated the potential for using AMDs for mitigation during windfarm construction, explored the types of acoustic signals that might be suitable for this application and reviewed the devices available for producing them in the field.

Following an extensive review, it was concluded that the use of AMDs in deterring animals from the danger zone could be a cost-effective way of mitigating against impacts.

But to allow the promise of AMDs to become a reality, further research on how different species respond to them is necessary. The authors also recommended studies to quantify the level of risk reduction that could be achieved by AMDs alone or as part of a larger mitigation process (Gordon *et al.,* 2007).

The last two studies commissioned by COWRIE – undertaken by Seamarco (in the Netherlands) and Subacoustech Ltd – sought to take the AMD review by SMRU Ltd further by aiming to quantify the performance of AMDs and to develop practical field equipment. Subacoustech examined a set of preselected devices to test for loudness and emitted frequencies to get an idea of the variability across and within device types. Seamarco performed experimental tests looking at the behavioural reactions of porpoises and seals towards AMDs in their captive facilities. Both projects kicked off in early 2010 and were completed in summer 2010.

Changes to the engineering design

Another way of reducing the impact of offshore windfarm sound is to alter the design from an engineering point of view so that sound levels are lower and the frequencies emitted are different and less severe.

In a desk-based study, BioConsult SH investigated engineering solutions (and associated costs) that could be used to mitigate against the effects of construction activities from offshore windfarms (Nehls *et al.,* 2007). The review examined methods such as prolonging the duration of the impact of the hammer on the pile as well as the use of bubble curtains around the pile driver.

One method described in more detail is the use of an inflatable piling sleeve which can be permanently mounted below the piling gate at the construction platform. The sleeve is meant to be inflated to a 50 mm layer of air during the piling operation. Initial tests indicated that the

The Aquatec AquaMARK 100 AMD – a porpoise deterrent pinger tested by Subacoustech as part of the project to measure variability amongst AMDs.
© Subacoustech Environmental Ltd

Engineering solutions to mitigate against the effects of construction activities from offshore windfarms: a foam-coated steel tube in measurement position.
© Nehls *et.al* COWRIE report ENG-01-2007

sleeve is expected to reach an attenuation of up to 20 dB broadband.

A second method involved a telescopic double-wall steel tube with a foam-filled interspace. A 100 mm foam layer was calculated to reach an attenuation of 15 dB broadband.

Both methods are considered compatible with the piling process and indicative costs are given.

The study by BioConsult SH is a first step into investigating mitigation measures from an engineering perspective. More tests are vital to investigate appropriate engineering techniques to mitigate against pile-driving pulses.

Conclusions

The COWRIE studies on sound effects have made a huge impact on the environmental management of offshore windfarms in the UK and elsewhere. They provided essential information on the sounds emitted during the construction and operation of marine wind turbines, without which initial assessment could have not been carried out.

The modelling studies triggered important discussions within the scientific community and beyond about impacts of offshore windfarms, and some of the results have been directly applied in regulation (e.g. restrictions on pile driving at herring and sole spawning areas in the UK during critical times of the year).

Experimental studies such as the playback experiments undertaken by Cefas have further implications for management and will hopefully pave the road to follow-up investigations to shed light on the characteristics of the response of marine life to pile driving and perhaps other windfarm sounds.

Finally, COWRIE's benchmark research on mitigation measures has already helped to reduce the impacts of offshore windfarm sound on marine life as, for example, AMDs are already used in some locations.

Engineering solutions to mitigate against the effects of construction activities from offshore windfarms: a double-wall model of a pile sleeve, containing 50 mm foam layer and test setup, including two hydrophones and piezo-electric transducer as sound source inside the sleeve model. © Nehls *et.al* COWRIE report ENG-01-2007

References

Gordon, J., Thompson, D., Gillespie, D., Lonergan, M., Calderan, S., Jaffey, B. and Todd, V. 2007. *Assessment of the potential for acoustic deterrents to mitigate the impact on marine mammals of underwater noise arising from the construction of offshore windfarms.* COWRIE Report DETER-01-07. Prepared for COWRIE Limited by Sea Mammal Research Unit (SMRU) Ltd. COWRIE Limited, London.

Mueller-Blenkle, C., McGregor, P., Gill, A.B., Andersson, M., Metcalfe, J., Bendall, V., Sigray, P. and Thomsen, F. 2010. *Effects of pile-driving noise on the behaviour of marine fish.* Prepared for COWRIE Limited. COWRIE Limited, London.

Nedwell, J.R. and Howell, D. 2004. *A review of offshore windfarm related underwater noise sources.* Subacoustech Report No. 544 R 0308. Prepared for COWRIE by Subacoustech Ltd. COWRIE, London.

Nedwell, J.R. and Brooker, A.G. 2008. *Measurement and assessment of background underwater noise and its comparison with noise from pin pile drilling operations during installation of the SeaGen tidal turbine device, Strangford Lough.* COWRIE Report SEAGEN-07-07. Prepared for COWRIE Limited by Subacoustech Ltd. COWRIE Limited, London.

Nedwell, J., Langworthy, J. and Howell, D. 2004. *Assessment of sub-sea acoustic noise and vibration from offshore wind turbines and its impact on marine wildlife; initial measurements of underwater noise during construction of offshore windfarms, and comparison with background noise.* Subacoustech Report No. 544 R 0424. Prepared for COWRIE by Subacoustech Ltd. COWRIE, London.

Nedwell, J.R., Parvin, S.J., Edwards, B., Workman, R., Brooker, A.G. and Kynoch, J.E. 2007. *Measurement and interpretation of underwater noise during construction and operation of offshore windfarms in UK waters.* COWRIE Report NOISE-03-2003. Subacoustech Report No. 544 R 0738. Prepared for COWRIE Limited by Subacoustech Ltd. COWRIE Limited, London.

Nehls, G., Betke, K., Eckelmann, S. and Ros, M. 2007. *Assessment and costs of potential engineering solutions for the mitigation of the impacts of underwater noise arising from the construction of offshore windfarms.* COWRIE Report ENG-01-2007. Prepared for COWRIE Limited by BioConsult SH, Husum, Germany. COWRIE Limited, London.

Thompson, P., Brookes, K., Cheney, B., Cândido, A., Bates, H., Richardson, N. and Barton, T. 2010. *Assessing the potential impact of oil and gas exploration operations on cetaceans in the Moray Firth.* First year report for DECC, Scottish Government, COWRIE and Oil & Gas UK by University of Aberdeen, Institute of Biological & Environmental Sciences, Lighthouse Field Station, Cromarty. DECC, London.

Thomsen, F., Lüdemann, K., Kafemann, R. and Piper, W. 2006. *Effects of offshore windfarm noise on marine mammals and fish.* Prepared for COWRIE Limited by biola (biologisch-landschaftsökologische arbeitsgemeinschaft) and IfAF (Institut für angewandte Fischbiologie GmbH), Hamburg, Germany. COWRIE Limited, London.

Fish and seabed communities

Gero Vella

Research commissioned by COWRIE has provided the first scientific evidence that electrosensitive species can detect and respond to the electromagnetic fields generated by windfarm power cables; ways of mitigating the impacts are being investigated

WHEN IDENTIFYING areas of priority research in 2002, COWRIE recognised a number of potential impacts from the development of offshore windfarms on fish and seabed communities including:

- the physical loss of seabed to turbines;
- disturbance and damage to seabed communities and the fish communities they support from construction or changes in sediment transport pathways and remobilisation of nutrients or contaminants.

The potential impact on habitats listed under Annex 1 of the EU Habitats Directive 92/43/EEC (e.g. 'shallow subtidal sandbanks' and the biogenic reefs formed by *Sabellaria*

spinulosa) was of particular concern due to the 'ecosystem function' of these habitats. However, it was also recognised that many of these potential impacts would be site-specific and that a wealth of information was available from parallel activities and industries (e.g. aggregates industry) on the magnitude and duration of such impacts and the potential for recoverability.

COWRIE identified two areas of concern for which there was a paucity of information:

- the potential impact of underwater noise and vibration during the construction and operation of windfarms;
- the potential impact of electromagnetic fields (EMF) generated by the intra-array and export power cables.

Sabellaria spinulosa, **biogenic reef, Wash Estuary. Reefs such as these are important habitats.** *Photograph courtesy of Centrica.* © Centrica Energy

The potential impact of underwater noise on sensitive marine wildlife groups was relatively well understood for some noisy marine activities such as seismic surveys, but relatively unknown for others such as low frequency sonar. COWRIE was concerned that the noise frequencies and intensity generated during the construction and operation of windfarms, and the magnitude of potential impacts, were not well understood. Similarly, on the subject of electromagnetic fields, some studies had documented the sensitivity of several electrosensitive species to high voltage direct current (HVDC) cables, but there were little data on the magnitude and impact of the alternating current (AC) cables proposed by the wind industry.

The characterisation of underwater noise generated by windfarm construction and operation, and the studies commissioned by COWRIE into identifying the magnitude of the impact on seabed communities, fish and marine mammals are considered in Chapter 4. This chapter therefore focuses on COWRIE research seeking greater understanding of the potential impact of electromagnetic fields on electrosensitive wildlife groups. It ends with an outline of recent research commissioned by COWRIE to identify practical ways in which to mitigate potential impacts.

Electromagnetic fields – background to the issue

A preliminary investigation of the potential impacts of offshore windfarm power cables on electrosensitive fish was carried out by the University of Liverpool in 2001 (Gill and Taylor, 2002). Owing to a paucity of information in the literature, a basic laboratory-based experiment was carried out to investigate the response of the dogfish, *Scyliorhinus canicula*, to electric fields generated by a direct current (DC)

A bull rout (*Myoxocephalus scorpius*) off the Lincolnshire coast. While fish species like the bull rout are of little commercial value, they play an important role in maintaining seabed communities that feed commercial stocks. The sensitivity of species such as this to electromagnetic fields is not well understood. *Photograph courtesy of Centrica.* © Centrica Energy

electrode placed in a seawater tank. Although only a pilot study, the results suggested that electrosensitive species such as the dogfish could be attracted to, or repelled from, electric fields generated by sub-sea cables. Experiments in Sweden confirmed that magnetically sensitive fish species such as eels and salmon reacted to the magnetic field generated by HVDC cables (Westerberg, 2000; Westerberg *et al.*, 2000).

COWRIE research on the effects of electromagnetic fields

Given the apparent lack of information and the potential significance of impacts, COWRIE identified electromagnetic fields as a priority research topic and recommended a two-phase approach to investigating their potential ecological impacts:

- **Phase 1** – a study to calculate the electromagnetic field generated by power cables at the seabed, assess the effects of burial and/or shielding and carry out some preliminary in situ measurements of the electromagnetic field generated by an existing sub-sea power cable;
- **Phase 2** – investigation of the actual impact of electromagnetic fields on the behaviour and ecology of electrosensitive and magnetically sensitive marine species through in situ experiments and monitoring.

Phase 1 study

The Phase 1 study was carried out by a consortium led by the Centre for Marine and Coastal Studies (CMACS) and including the University of Liverpool and Econnect Limited (CMACS, 2003). The study's objective was to model mathematically the likely electromagnetic field emitted from a 132 kV three-phase submarine AC power cable buried in a sandy seabed at a depth of one metre. Its

aim was to answer the question of whether or not an EMF was produced that could be detected by electrosensitive species.

Discussions with cable manufacturers and electrical engineers suggested that a power cable with perfect shielding does not generate an electric field directly. The results of the model simulations supported this conclusion, but the modelling also demonstrated that the alternating current in the cable generates a magnetic field in the local environment. This in turn generates an induced electric field close to the cable within the range detectable by electrosensitive fish species such as elasmobranchs (sharks, skates and rays). This result had not been anticipated. In the model used, the strength of the induced electric field (Figure 5.1) was within the range of detection of electrosensitive species such as benthic sharks.

As the magnetic field generated by the alternating current was emitted over several to tens of metres irrespective of the type of material the cables were buried in, it was concluded that cable burial had little effect in mitigating impacts other than to provide a physical barrier between communities on the seabed and the strongest induced electric fields lying close to the surface of the cable. Options for mitigation through changes in permeability and conductivity of shielding materials were explored and a method of measuring electric fields *in situ* was developed.

The project had been successful in that it had answered the question as to whether an electromagnetic field was produced by a windfarm power cable that was detectable by electrosensitive species such as benthic sharks. But the magnitude and consequences of any impact remained unknown.

The project team recommended further investigation of the potential impacts through a combination of further modelling, but more importantly, the in situ observations that COWRIE had initially identified for Phase 2. The team also noted the importance of collating and inferring information from planned monitoring studies in the UK and abroad to investigate the impacts of offshore windfarms and associated cabling on fish populations. At the time of the study very few of these monitoring programmes had begun but, by the time the Phase 1 report had been reviewed and finalised, the situation had begun to change and more information was becoming available. In light of this COWRIE decided to commission a literature review to update the Phase 1 study with the most recent information and to identify the priorities before commencing Phase 2. This review became known as the 'Phase 1.5 review'.

Phase 1.5 review

The review by Cranfield University and CMACS began by collating:

- up-to-date information on the biology of electrosensitive and magnetically sensitive species;
- information from the offshore windfarm industry from discussions and published documents.

Information from the first international conference dedicated to assessing the environmental impact of offshore windfarms was also incorporated; 'Offshore Wind Farms and the Environment, Horns Rev and Nysted' was held at Billund in Denmark in September 2004.

The collated information provided the material for the series of literature reviews of specific topics presented in the final report (Gill *et al.*, 2005). These reviews formed the basis for a set of recommendations for future COWRIE research relating to electromagnetic fields.

The review of windfarm Environmental Statements and monitoring programmes highlighted inconsistencies in the way developers had approached the issue of electromagnetic effects and a number of

important misconceptions were highlighted. The main reason for these was thought to be a lack of clear scientific guidance on the species of concern and (potential) significance of effects on receptor species. To improve this situation, the review provided comprehensive guidance for windfarm developers on:

- priority species of concern;
- the identification and assessment of potential impacts;
- standard monitoring techniques.

The Phase 1.5 review also considered the priorities for further research, concluding that the magnitude of potential impacts could only be fully understood through mesocosm studies that allow the reaction of sensitive species to electromagnetic fields in the 'real world' to be scientifically documented (a large sea pen confining species of concern in their natural environment is an example of a mesocosm).

Furthermore, these mesocosm studies should be supplemented by site-specific monitoring studies both after construction and at operational windfarms.

Phase 2 study

Given the conservation and commercial importance of a number of the priority species identified in the Phase 1 review and concern over the continuing paucity of data regarding this potential impact, COWRIE decided to go ahead with Phase 2. The aim was to make use of live fish in controlled conditions that simulated the natural environment as fully as possible so that behavioural responses in the wild could be investigated. The project was undertaken by a consortium consisting of Cranfield University, CMACS, Cefas and the Centre for Intelligent Monitoring Systems (CIMS) at the University of Liverpool (Gill *et al.*, 2009).

Two mesocosms of 40 metres diameter and 5 metres deep were constructed just off the shore at Ardtoe, Scotland. Sub-sea power cables capable of generating electromagnetic fields characteristic of those generated at offshore windfarms were laid dissecting each mesocosm and buried to a depth of up to one metre. Three species sensitive to electromagnetic fields and recorded in several offshore windfarms – Thornback ray (*Raja clavata*), Spurdog (*Squalus acanthias*) and lesser spotted dogfish (*Scyliorhinus canicula*) – were placed in each mesocosm. Ultrasonic telemetry technology was used to detect the real-time movements of individual fish within each mesocosm in relation to the energised sub-sea power cable. The comparativeness of the electromagnetic field in the mesocosm was confirmed against measurements of the actual electromagnetic fields generated

by feeder cables from several operating windfarms; because electromagnetic field strength is a factor of a number of different parameters (e.g. the specification of the power cable), it was necessary to ensure that the electromagnetic field generated by the cables in the mesocosms was indeed comparable with the electromagnetic fields generated in actual windfarms.

The simulations were designed to answer the primary research question: do electromagnetically sensitive organisms respond to man-made electromagnetic fields of the type and magnitude generated by offshore windfarms? The answer was 'yes'.

Despite the technical and practical challenges, the study provided the first ever scientific evidence that electrosensitive fish

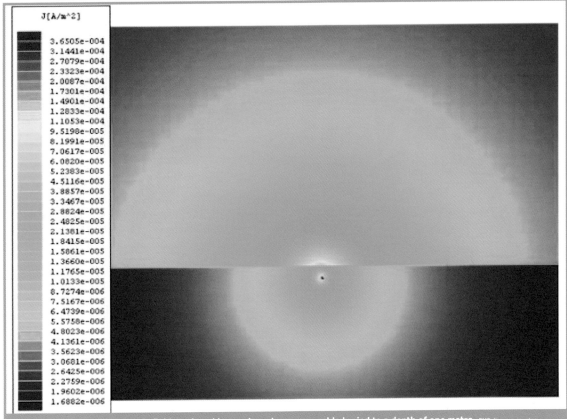

Figure 5.1 The induced electric field produced by a submarine power cable buried to a depth of one metre. *EMF diagram courtesy of CMACS. © CMACS LTD.*

respond to the electromagnetic field generated by sub-sea power cables of the type used at offshore windfarms. Furthermore, the response recorded was localised and appeared to be attractive rather that repelling. However, the report's authors cautioned that:

- it was not possible to draw conclusions on whether the electromagnetic field encountered by the test species could have a positive or negative impact;
- such a question can only be answered through further specific studies and ideally through monitoring at offshore windfarm sites with appropriate analysis over time.

Mitigating impacts on fish and seabed communities

Despite several topics being identified as priority research, COWRIE had not commissioned any research that considered

Weighing and measuring benthic sharks and rays before returning them to the southern North Sea. Shark species such as these can detect the induced electric field generated by windfarm power cables. *Photograph courtesy of Centrica. © Centrica Energy*

how to mitigate the potential impact of offshore windfarm development on fish and seabed communities. This was because the cross-government Research Advisory Group (RAG) set up to identify and co-ordinate research into the key impacts of Round 2 windfarms was funding a number of research projects in parallel to COWRIE including, for example, a review of the reef effect of offshore windfarm structures and the potential for enhancement and mitigation (Linley et al., 2008).

However, in a late addition to its portfolio of projects, COWRIE asked Ichthys Marine Ecological Consultants to investigate options and opportunities to mitigate the potential impact of offshore windfarm developments on commercial fisheries through creation of a 'toolbox' of identified mitigation options (Blyth-Skyrme, 2010). This toolbox will help developers, fishermen, regulators, statutory advisors and marine resource managers when discussing present and future windfarm developments, as well as during future consideration of marine spatial planning. The project, which was developed in collaboration with several Sea Fisheries Committees, examined:

- habitat distribution;
- fisheries biology and management;
- potentially novel techniques for habitat remediation and enhancement.

Consultations and workshops will endeavour to ensure acceptability of the project findings to the fishing and renewables industries.

Conclusions

In trying to understand the significance of electromagnetic fields for sensitive species, COWRIE had set itself a very difficult task. Although the significance of electromagnetic fields and the magnitude of any impact (positive or negative) remain unknown, the research commissioned by COWRIE has provided invaluable insights which have been used extensively in the UK and in Europe. The successes of this research include:

- identifying the generation of induced electric fields of a strength known to be detectable by some species of benthic elasmobranchs, confirming the 'potential' for an impact to exist;
- guidance for the wind industry and regulators on the priority species of concern, the potential impacts and methods for sampling electromagnetic fields and sampling methods for sensitive species;
- the first evidence that electrosensitive species can detect and react to electromagnetic fields characteristic of offshore windfarms in the marine environment through a particularly ambitious and practically challenging experimental design.

As we move into the third licensing round of offshore wind, the number of gaps and uncertainties in our knowledge of the interaction between offshore windfarms and the environment is decreasing. The research identified, prioritised and funded by COWRIE has played a fundamental role in reducing these gaps and uncertainties.

References

Blyth-Skyrme, R.E. 2010. *Options and opportunities for marine fisheries mitigation associated with windfarms.* Final report for COWRIE contract FISHMITIG09. COWRIE Ltd, London.

Centre for Marine and Coastal Studies (CMACS). 2003. *A baseline assessment of electromagnetic fields generated by offshore windfarm cables.* COWRIE-EMF-01-2002. Prepared for COWRIE by University of Liverpool and ECONNECT Ltd.

Gill, A.B. and Taylor, H. 2002. *The potential effects of electromagnetic fields generated by cabling between offshore wind turbines upon elasmobranch fishes.* Report to the Countryside Council for Wales (CCW Contract Science Report No. 488).

Gill, A.B., Gloyne-Phillips, I., Neal, K.J. and Kimber, J.A. 2005. *The potential effects of electromagnetic fields generated by sub-sea power cables associated with offshore windfarm developments on electrically and magnetically sensitive marine organisms – a review.* COWRIE-EM FIELD 2-06-2004. Prepared for COWRIE by Cranfield University and Centre for Marine and Coastal Studies Ltd.

Gill, A.B., Huang, Y., Gloyne-Philips, I., Metcalfe, J., Quayle, V., Spencer, J. and Wearmouth, V. 2009. COWRIE 2.0 *Electromagnetic Fields (EMF) Phase 2: EMF-sensitive fish response to EM emissions from sub-sea electricity cables of the type used by the offshore renewable energy industry.* COWRIE-EMF-1-06. Prepared for COWRIE Limited by Cranfield University, CEFAS, CIMS Centre for Intelligent Monitoring Systems, University of Liverpool and Centre for Marine and Coastal Studies Ltd.

Linley, E.A.S., Wilding T.A., Black K., Hawkins A.J.S. and Mangi, S. 2008. *Review of the reef effects of offshore windfarm structures and their potential for enhancement and mitigation.* Report from PML Applications Ltd and the Scottish Association for Marine Science to the Department for Business, Enterprise and Regulatory Reform (BERR) under Contract No. RFCA/005/0029P.

Westerberg, H. 2000. 'Effect of HVDC cables on eel orientation'. In: Merck, T. and von Nordheim, H. (ed). *Technishe Eingriffe in marine Lebensraüme.* Bundesamt für Naturschutz, Bonn.

Westerberg, H. and Begout-Anras, M.L. 2000. 'Orientation of silver eel (*Anguilla anguilla*) in a disturbed geomagnetic field'. In: *Advances in Fish Telemetry*, Proceedings of the Third Conference on Fish Telemetry in Europe (ed. A. Moore and I. Russell), Norwich, June 1999. Cefas, Lowestoft.

6

Marine mammals

Frank Thomsen

A combination of high resolution visual airplane surveys and passive acoustic monitoring techniques is recommended to determine the number and distribution of marine mammals at offshore sites; such methods also help to measure changes resulting from human activity

MORE THAN 20 cetacean and three seal species reside in and/or travel through northwest European waters. A number of the cetacean species live mainly in relatively deep waters offshore and might therefore travel only occasionally in areas of prospective offshore windfarm development.

Harbour porpoises (*Phocoena phocoena*) and common seals (*Phoca vitulina*) are in principle the most common species and thus are investigated most in impact assessments for offshore windfarms.

Other candidates for a more comprehensive assessment with respect to northern European waters include:
- grey seal (*Halichoerus grypus*);
- bottlenose dolphin (*Tursiops truncatus*);
- common dolphin (*Delphinus delphis*);
- whitebeaked dolphin (*Lagenorhynchus albirostris*);
- Risso's dolphin (*Grampus griseus*);
- killer whale (*Orcinus orca*);
- minke whale (*Balaenoptera acutorostrata*).

These species are seen regularly in some coastal areas with the bottlenose dolphin forming resident populations in some areas off the west and east coasts of the UK.

However one should be cautious in narrowing down the number of species impacted by future developments too much as windfarms might well be planned in deeper waters with more species in the radius of potential impact.

Most of the impacts from offshore windfarms on marine mammals are thought to be related to sound emissions. There may be indirect effects, as offshore windfarms could lead to changes in local fish fauna due to the creation of artificial reefs and more direct impacts via visual disturbance. If and to what extent electromagnetic fields generated by offshore windfarm cables might disturb cetaceans is also unknown. However these are rather speculative areas which would need further exploration in desk-based assessments.

COWRIE studies on sound-related impacts are covered in Chapter 4. This chapter looks at projects dealing with the huge uncertainties in the abundance and distribution of marine mammals at marine construction sites. Another area where COWRIE funded studies to improve knowledge was the investigation of methods to measure change due to human impacts.

Survey techniques

High resolution video

In 2008 COWRIE commissioned HiDef Aerial Survey Ltd to undertake high resolution video surveys of seabirds and marine mammals off the Norfolk coast (Hexter, 2009a) and at Rhyl Flats off the North Wales coast (Hexter, 2009b). After initial tests using a camera mounted on a helicopter, further trials were undertaken using survey airplanes.

The use of high definition video techniques in surveys is relatively recent and could provide some important improvements to data collection from visual surveys in terms of reliability as species identification can be verified after the survey. Another advantage of video sampling is that aerial surveys can be undertaken at higher altitudes, which increases the safety of the survey crew and is less disturbing for the animals being recorded.

A twin-engine, high winged airplane with bubble windows on each side is often used for aerial surveys of marine mammals. © Werner Piper

The results of the trials are promising with harbour porpoises detected in Rhyl Flats and harbour porpoises, common seals and even dolphins documented off Norfolk – an area where previous surveys indicated a very low abundance of marine mammals.

Passive acoustic monitoring

In May 2009 the Department of Energy and Climate Change (DECC), with co-funding from the Scottish Government, Oil & Gas UK and COWRIE, asked the Institute of Biological & Environmental Sciences at the University of Aberdeen to carry out a three-year study on cetaceans in the Moray Firth. The study aims to provide baseline data on the occurrence of cetaceans in the Moray Firth to:
- support the assessment and mitigation of proposed offshore windfarm construction and seismic surveys;
- assess the impacts of seismic exploration on these species.

The first year report (Thompson *et al.* 2010) presents the results of surveys to:
- assess the relative abundance of bottlenose dolphins and other cetaceans;

- develop procedures for measuring ambient and seismic sound levels (see Chapter 4 re novel ambient noise recordings).

The team used passive acoustic monitoring techniques to provide data on spatial and temporal changes in the occurrence of dolphins and porpoises in the Moray Firth. A specialised device – an automated porpoise detector or POD – was used for this part of the study. PODs are data loggers that can be deployed over long periods of time and which automatically register the high frequency click sounds that porpoises use for navigation and finding fish.

The acoustic surveys were complemented by visual line-transect surveys in the outer Moray Firth. Line-transect surveys are another technique that is often used when estimating

Field researcher with automated porpoise click-detector (POD). © University of Aberdeen

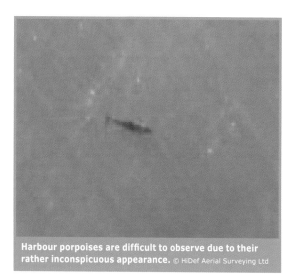

Harbour porpoises are difficult to observe due to their rather inconspicuous appearance. © HiDef Aerial Surveying Ltd

cetacean abundance. Here a study area is surveyed using pre-determined lines. Any animals along the line are registered and the distance of the sighting to the transect line is estimated using specialised equipment. The distances plotted together result in a strip width for the survey, and together with the number of animals and the overall distance travelled, can be used to calculate animal numbers per area. This is then extrapolated to the whole study area to give abundance estimates.

The results from the first year of investigations show that dolphins were more often acoustically detected in the inner Moray Firth and along the coastal survey area than in the central part of the outer Moray Firth. It is not possible to determine which species of dolphins were detected by the PODs, but looking at results from previous work and dedicated surveys, it appears likely that the detections in the inner Moray Firth are of

bottlenose dolphins whereas, in the outer Moray Firth, white beaked dolphins were registered. Harbour porpoises were detected much more commonly throughout the whole study area, with the highest level of detections in the outer Moray Firth. Dolphins were seen during only two of the visual line-transect surveys whereas harbour porpoises were encountered on all surveys. These initial results will be used in assessing the likely exposure of porpoises and dolphins to sounds from planned seismic surveys in the area. The research programme will continue until 2012.

Counting

Another important question is how to measure change in numbers of cetacean groups that are experiencing impacts from human activities. Other investigations have shown that abundance estimates for marine mammals

Cetaceans can best be observed at very low sea states. © Lighthouse Field Station, University of Aberdeen

such as, for example, for the most common species, harbour porpoises, are very variable. Detecting whether a population in a given area shows a change in numbers over time is therefore challenging.

At COWRIE's request BioConsult SH analysed methodologies for measuring and assessing potential changes in marine mammal behaviour, abundance or distribution arising from the construction, operation and decommissioning of offshore windfarms (Diederichs *et al.,* 2008). Even defining the scope of such an investigation proved challenging as impacts could occur at various scales. For example sound impacts during construction might be of short duration but long range, whereas during operation impacts are perhaps short range but permanent.

The team concluded that in high density areas, where relatively robust density estimates can be obtained, changes in cetacean populations could be detected by a small number of visual surveys – either from airplanes or ships. The precision of estimates from ship surveys could be increased using hydrophones (underwater microphones) towed behind the survey vessel. In such ways, submerged cetaceans could be at least detected acoustically. Automatic click detectors can also be used and, depending on the amount of clicks recorded, changes of 30% could be identified using 3–11 samples (defined as the number of monitoring positions per month).

In general a combination of visual and acoustic surveys was recommended – a suggestion that has been realised in many field

Visual surveys, from ships or planes, can be used to estimate changes in cetacean populations resulting from offshore wind farms in areas of high population density. © University of Aberdeen

studies including, for example, the current one in the Moray Firth.

Conclusions

Besides the extensive studies on sound impacts, COWRIE's marine mammal programme concentrated on survey techniques and a desk-based review of methods of investigating changes in cetacean populations. The use of high definition video techniques could become quite promising in future visual surveys on marine mammals and the application of automated porpoise detectors has shed interesting insights into the distribution of porpoises and bottlenose dolphins in the Moray Firth. Further work on methods to measure changes in cetacean populations will contribute to a much more thorough design of field impact studies and could help protect cetaceans from human activities.

References

Diederichs, A., Nehls, G., Daehne, M., Adler, S., Koschinski, S. and Verfuss, U. 2008. *Methodologies for measuring and assessing potential changes in marine mammal behaviour, abundance or distribution arising from the construction, operation and decommissioning of offshore windfarms*. Prepared for COWRIE Limited by BioConsult SH, Husum, Germany. COWRIE Limited, London.

Hexter, R. 2009a. *High resolution video survey of seabirds and mammals in the Norfolk area*. COWRIE Report ZONE-01-09. Prepared for COWRIE Limited by HiDef Aerial Surveying Limited. COWRIE Limited, London.

Hexter, R. 2009b. *High resolution video survey of seabirds and mammals in the Rhyl Flats area*. COWRIE Report RTD-01-09. Prepared for COWRIE Limited by HiDef Aerial Surveying Limited. COWRIE Limited, London.

Thompson, P., Brookes, K., Cheney, B., Cândido, A., Bates, H., Richardson, N. and Barton, T. 2010. *Assessing the potential impact of oil and gas exploration operations on cetaceans in the Moray Firth*. First year report for DECC, Scottish Government, COWRIE and Oil & Gas UK by University of Aberdeen, Institute of Biological & Environmental Sciences, Lighthouse Field Station, Cromarty. DECC, London.

7 Birds

Dr Rowena Langston, Dr Sophy Allen and Zoe Crutchfield

COWRIE has developed guidance on offshore surveys, study methods and impact assessment, commissioned work to advance the use of high definition digital imagery for bird surveys, and undertaken research on species considered particularly vulnerable to offshore windfarm development

IN 2001, offshore wind energy was a novel industry and there were uncertainties as to the associated environmental impacts. COWRIE played an instrumental role in bringing together expertise from government departments, their nature conservation advisors, industry and the RSPB to provide guidance on study methods and to contribute to the growing knowledge of the interactions between birds and windfarms.

To achieve this COWRIE supported the development of advances in the study of birds in the marine environment. When identifying possible research projects, the main risks for birds were considered to be:

- collision with the rotor blades or other parts of the turbine infrastructure, or injury/death resulting from turbulence associated with operational wind turbines;
- disturbance/displacement equating to habitat loss which might be temporary or longer term;
- direct or indirect effects on habitats or prey species;

- barriers to movement – intercepting regular flights between feeding and nesting areas or disrupting longer migratory flights, which might increase the energetic costs of such flights.

Not all bird species are equally vulnerable and a variety of factors influence risk including the location of a windfarm and the uses made by birds of a specific area such as for feeding or resting.

COWRIE developed a range of guidance covering offshore surveys, study methods and impact assessment (Figure 7.1). It also commissioned research on several species considered particularly vulnerable to various aspects of offshore windfarm development such as red-throated diver and common scoter (sensitive to disturbance) and breeding terns and migratory whooper swans (among species of concern in relation to collision risk with wind turbines). Later studies contributed to surveys of offshore windfarms, mainly to test novel survey methods.

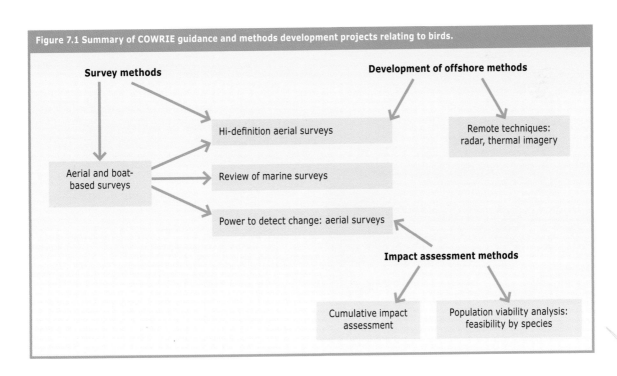

Figure 7.1 Summary of COWRIE guidance and methods development projects relating to birds.

Survey methods

The development of offshore windfarms necessitated an increase in bird survey effort by developers and government to provide information for Strategic Environmental Assessment (SEA) and environmental impact assessment (EIA) processes. COWRIE recognised that standardisation of existing survey techniques and development of guidance on new and emerging methods would be of benefit. However, it was acknowledged that:

- different survey methods were needed for different species and locations;
- the appropriate survey technique would depend on the questions to be answered.

Aerial and boat-based surveys

Standardised seabirds at sea census techniques

One of the first projects commissioned by COWRIE was a comparison of ship and aerial sampling methods for marine birds, and their applicability to offshore windfarms (Camphuysen *et al.*, 2004). This study, led by a team from the Royal Netherlands Institute for Sea Research, sought to develop standardised survey protocols to provide confidence to regulators and developers alike that the data collected provided a reliable picture of the birds using windfarm areas.

The MV *Southern Star* is a research vessel that conforms to COWRIE guidelines for ship-based surveys. © Ciaran Cronin/Emu Ltd/SMart Wind Ltd.

The report recommended methodologies for both aerial and boat-based surveys (Table 7.1) as well as recognising that one of the most important factors in any survey design is establishing at the outset what the aims and objectives are. It was also noted that the cost-effectiveness of boat-based surveys might be enhanced if the vessel was also used for marine mammal surveys and equipped to record conditions such as temperature, fluorescence and salinity.

Further refinement of survey techniques

As work on offshore windfarms continued and the COWRIE guidance was put into action, it became apparent that further refinement of the survey techniques was required to ensure their applicability – especially as developments moved further offshore.

A review of assessment methodologies carried out for COWRIE by the British Trust for Ornithology (BTO) assessed the extent to which recommendations in the 2004 guidance had been followed and provided more rigorous guidelines for the analytical techniques that should be used to analyse survey data (Maclean *et al.*, 2009[1]). Examination of eight Environmental Statements for offshore windfarms found that the surveys had generally followed the majority of the recommendations, with some adhering to the guidance more strictly than others. The report stressed the importance of accurately recording survey techniques in an Environmental Statement so that readers fully understood how data were collected and whether they have been properly applied to assess impacts.

The **boat-based surveys** had followed most of the recommendations in the 2004 guidance except that some surveyors had used an alternative method where the exact timing of bird sightings were recorded rather than

---

1 There is an updated version of this report with some clarifications.

assigning birds to time intervals (this method improves the accuracy of the location assigned to the sighting but is incompatible with current nature conservation databases). Others had developed an alternative method for carrying out snapshot point counts, whereby counts were conducted at regular distance intervals (measured using GPS) rather than at regular time intervals; this meant that any variation in speed of the boat would not affect the distance between snapshot points. The majority of the surveys had not followed the recommendations that an area at least six times the size of the proposed windfarm should be surveyed and that two observers should be present per observation platform.

Visual aerial surveys are a useful way to cover large sea areas in a short space of time. © Anne Harrison

Further recommendations for boat-based surveys made in the 2009 report included:

- assigning observers an ID code;
- recording sea states and viewing conditions.

The recommendation that a minimum of two observers be available was reinforced and, during longer daylight hours, three observers were recommended to allow rest periods.

It was recognised that, for Round 3 Zones, the recommendation that transects should not be more than two nautical miles apart might not be practical. However, it was suggested that if surveys were undertaken at a coarser resolution, hydrographic data should be collected at the same time to allow for better prediction of bird densities across the entire zone. It was also acknowledged that, for the larger zones, to survey six times the area of the windfarm would not be practicable. The report's authors advocated surveying the entire development zone in one session, adopting the most appropriate transect separation to achieve this.

The 2009 review noted that the majority of **aerial surveys** had been undertaken by one operator, The Wildfowl and Wetlands Trust (WWT), using standardised methodologies as recommended in the 2004 report. The only variations were flight height and the use of four

Table 7.1 Recommended methodologies for surveys (Camphuysen *et al.*, 2004).	
Type	**Recommendations**
Boat-based	• A line-transect methodology with a maximum strip width of 300 metres. • No observations in sea state* 5 or above for seabirds and above sea state 3 for marine mammals. • A vessel with a forward viewing platform preferably 10 metres above sea level (range 5–25 metres) and a speed of 10 knots (range 5–15 knots). • Observers with adequate identification skills for offshore surveys.
Aerial	• A twin-engine aircraft (for safety and endurance) with high wings for excellent visibility. • A line-transect methodology with sub-bands. • Transects a minimum of 2 km apart to avoid double counting but maximising coverage. • Flight speed of 185 km/hour at an altitude of 80 metres. • Two trained observers – one covering each side of the aircraft – with continuous recording on Dictaphones and global positioning system (GPS) recording at least every five seconds. • No observations in sea states above 3.

* Sea state describes the sea surface conditions from mirror calm (0 Beaufort), through tiny ripples (1), small waves (2; no whitecaps), small waves (3; with few whitecaps), moderate waves (4; numerous whitecaps), larger waves with whitecaps forming bands (5), and large waves with dominant whitecaps forming broad bands (6) (Camphuysen *et al.*, 2004).

rather than three distance bands. As with boat-based surveys, the review recommended ensuring observers were assigned an ID code, and that sea states and viewing conditions were recorded. There was also a recommendation that, during aerial surveys, attempts should be made to distinguish between birds in flight naturally and those that might have been flushed by the aircraft.

The **data analysis methods** were also reviewed. Most surveys (aerial and boat-based) had been conducted all year round for two years, although there was little consistency in the survey months. The 2009 report recommended that:

- boat-based surveys should be undertaken for a minimum of two years on a monthly basis;
- aerial surveys should be undertaken at least eight times per year (three times in winter and five times in summer, though this would depend on the species expected);
- data should be corrected to account for the area surveyed in relation to the study area;
- all aerial/boat-based transect data should be corrected to account for undetected birds.

The difficulty of **assessing the significance of impacts** was recognised and it was recommended that expert judgement guided by best available information be used as the main tool for reaching conclusions. A matrix approach where the magnitude of, and sensitivity to, impacts are cross-tabulated to assess the significance of impacts quantitatively was suggested, alongside a qualitative assessment (employing expert judgement) of the sensitivity of the species to the particular impact in question.

In the absence of more detailed information, the key recommendations for impact assessment from the 2009 review were as follows:

- Assume all birds are displaced from the windfarm area when determining the magnitude of displacement impacts and the magnitude of impacts due to habitat loss.

- Determine the magnitude of impacts due to barrier effects using two criteria – the number of birds likely to be flying through the windfarm and the extent to which the windfarm is likely to act as a barrier.
- Use a standard method for calculating the number of birds at risk of collision applicable to the collision risk model developed by Band (2000).

Conclusions

The standardisation and quality of developer-led aerial and boat-based survey techniques has greatly improved during COWRIE's lifetime. A key message from its research is that understanding how the data will be analysed, assessed and used in impact assessment is crucial when designing surveys (aerial or visual). If data are collected to allow future monitoring it is vital that the statistical robustness of the data collection/analysis to detect change is assessed **before** the survey begins.

It is now generally recognised that boat-based and aerial survey techniques are complementary. Aerial surveys are useful for covering large sea areas in a short space of time (thus reducing the risk of double counting or displacement of birds) and boat-based surveys are useful for species discrimination and the collection of behavioural data.

High-definition survey techniques

The initial review of survey techniques undertaken for COWRIE in 2004 had concluded that aerial survey techniques have the advantage of being able to survey large areas in a cost-effective manner. However, technical difficulties with visual aerial survey techniques such as health and safety restrictions on minimum flight height and the implications on the quality of survey data from increasing flight elevation were subsequently recognised. One potential solution identified by COWRIE was the use of high-definition (HD) imagery which could produce fully auditable outputs based on recorded HD video or stills footage that were analysed post flight. It was envisaged that this technique would be useful for post-construction surveys where overflights of windfarm areas could be undertaken at a higher elevation than traditional visual aerial surveys.

Initial trial

COWRIE therefore commissioned HiDef Aerial Surveying Limited to investigate whether high-definition techniques provided the anticipated advantages over traditional visual aerial surveys and to highlight any disadvantages or difficulties encountered. A trial survey was carried out at St Bees Head in Cumbria in August 2007 (Mellor *et al.*, 2007).

The system deployed by HiDef Aerial Surveying Limited uses a gyroscopically stabilised camera mount to eliminate aircraft vibration, thus enabling the use of high magnification lenses. This in turn allows the aircraft or helicopter to fly at greater distances from the birds. The video is coupled to a GPS logging system that associates a geographical location with each video frame, enabling subsequent statistical analysis of the spatial distribution of birds.

In most cases, the system provided sufficient detail to enable reliable identification of birds. However, there were some difficulties in operating the video equipment in the manner required by the trial. Recommendations were made for further development of hi-definition technology, some of which were taken forward in further studies funded by COWRIE.

Full-scale trial

Following on from the work in 2007, COWRIE commissioned HiDef Aerial Surveying Limited to carry out a full-scale trial at Shell Flats in the Irish Sea off Blackpool in March 2008 (Mellor and Mahler, 2008). This trial aimed to:
- demonstrate the ability of the technique to reliably survey the more sensitive species of waterbird such as common scoter *Melanitta nigra* or red-throated diver *Gavia stellata*;
- compare the output of the HD video with data from other surveys to provide insights into the technique's performance;

One of the survey planes used during aerial surveys flown by HiDef Aerial Surveying Limited. © Giles Aviation Ltd

- undertake a large-scale trial to demonstrate the consistency of the technique and the usefulness of the data;
- demonstrate the feasibility of an aeroplane rather than a helicopter as the survey platform;
- test the technical refinements proposed as a result of the first trial.

The aeroplane was found to be well-suited to the task. It provided a more stable, quieter and more comfortable environment for operators, used less fuel, and cost significantly less per hour to hire. It was also noted that there are many more twin-engine aircraft available for this type of surveying than for visual aerial surveys.

The recommendations from the initial trial report for control of focus, image size and contrast were employed and resulted in significant improvement in video quality overall. Focus was still the main issue (especially over flat seas) and it was suggested that focus, zoom and camera angle could be locked without adverse impact on the survey quality. The target image width of 30 metres identified during the first trial was found to be pessimistic and the image width was increased to 40 metres alongside the other improvements in quality. This adjustment confers a 30% increase in coverage rate.

Large numbers of common scoter were encountered during the survey and showed no awareness of the aircraft when the plane was flown at an altitude of 600 metres. At 210 metres the birds were thought to be aware of the aircraft, but the vast majority remained on the water. It was concluded that, if the survey altitude was kept above 270 metres, scoter would not take flight.

A comparison of the HD video trial data with data from surveys undertaken by the Department for Business, Enterprise and Regulatory Reform (BERR) and WWT between 2004 and 2007 found very good agreement in terms of the spatial distribution of birds, although population estimates were half those from the WWT surveys.

Review workshop

The review of assessment methodologies for offshore windfarms (Maclean *et al.*, 2009) provided an initial review of the use of high-definition cameras. A workshop with key users, developers and regulators was held in July 2009; the workshop report (Thaxter and Burton, 2009) provided a comprehensive update, reviewing the trials of HD imagery and recommending survey protocols for HD imagery of seabirds and marine mammals. Information on trials was obtained from:
- APEM Limited;
- Danish National Environmental Research Institute (NERI);
- HiDef Aerial Surveying Limited;
- RSK Group Limited;
- University of St Andrews.

Those attending the workshop recognised that further methodological development was required, but agreed that the protocols used should depend on:
- the species present;
- the aims of the particular survey, e.g. site characterisation, baseline EIA, before and after control impact analysis (BACI), gradient effect, to inform Appropriate Assessments or for Common Standards Monitoring.

For baseline surveys, recommendations for minimum standards included:
- use of colour images for all surveys;
- not undertaking surveys in low cloud or adverse weather conditions;
- a minimum resolution of 5 cm (NB 3 cm is used routinely now);
- a minimum flight height of 450 metres to avoid disturbance to birds (if no disturbance was noted, this could be lowered when

increased resolution for improved species discrimination was required).

Other recommendations from the workshop included:
- using standardised Joint Nature Conservation Committee (JNCC) species groupings (Webb, 2010) to allow comparison with other survey techniques;
- exposure to be optimised for specific species when conducting species-specific surveys;
- use of automation for processing images.

For survey design and analysis, it was concluded that:
- survey methodologies should be maintained between consecutive surveys if a before and after assessment is required;
- different methodologies should only be used if statistical comparison is possible and there is no evidence of bias in survey estimates;
- BACI surveys should also be designed with the ability to detect a halving or doubling of the population as a minimum benchmark.

It was recognised that the power to detect change is not only based on the percentage of the region covered but also related to the number of sampling units, e.g. transect strips surveyed and their spacing. Ideally, all survey areas/zones should be covered in one day. For quality control, two or more adequately trained and experienced observers should assess the images independently.

Conclusions

Over the last decade, our knowledge of the use of high-definition aerial survey methods for bird and marine mammal surveys has greatly increased and a good deal of information on the effectiveness and operation of surveys has been published by COWRIE. High-definition imagery can reduce the time taken to survey for birds and marine mammals. It also allows post-construction monitoring to be undertaken using the same protocols as baseline data collection, providing greater potential for BACI studies to produce data of real value.

Application of high-definition aerial surveys

As part of the development of survey techniques and to support the deployment of Round 2 and 3 windfarms, COWRIE commissioned a number of aerial surveys to compare or develop techniques in Round 2/3 windfarm areas. These are summarised below.

Review of survey results for avian abundance for Round 3, Norfolk Region

Two aerial surveys in the Norfolk offshore windfarm area in the spring of 2009 were compared by a team from the Centre for Research into Ecological and Environmental Modelling, University of St Andrews (Burt *et al.*, 2009).

The region was sub-divided into eight blocks or strata. One survey employed on-board observers and surveyed over five days, while a second survey used digital video technology to collect bird detections over a three-day period. Abundance estimates were obtained using conventional distance sampling estimators as well as density models for the visual surveys. Strip transect methods as well as density surface models were used to compute abundance estimates for the digital video surveys. Species were divided into divers, gulls and seabird categories rather than producing estimates for each species.

The report concluded that:
- both data acquisition methods and survey design can be improved to enhance the precision of abundance estimates using digital techniques;

- the survey design should pay attention to the encounter rate variability (differences in the number of animals detected between transects), which drives much of the uncertainty associated with these surveys and their power to detect change.

Survey of seabirds and mammals in the Moray Firth, Hastings, West Isle of Wight and Bristol Channel Areas

The aim of this survey was to gather suitable datasets on the number and distribution of seabirds at and around the surveyed windfarm sites in support of the environmental impact assessment for Round 3 Zones 1, 6, 7 and 8 (see Figure 1.1). The technical report (Hexter, 2009a) includes detailed survey specification such as transect pattern alongside the output maps for each region and output data. This information was intended for use by regulators, developers and other interested parties when assessing potential impacts to birds from Round 3 developments.

Surveys of seabirds and mammals in the Rhyl Flats Area

This survey off the North Wales coast sought to further demonstrate the feasibility of using the HD video technology to survey for sensitive species such as red-throated divers, thereby seeking to increase confidence in high-definition survey techniques (Hexter, 2009b). Fifteen divers were identified from video data, giving a population estimate of 75 which was in line with previous population estimates. The survey results were used by regulators, developers and other interested parties, and in the development of guidance for high-definition surveys.

Surveys of seabirds and mammals in the Norfolk Area

The aim of this survey, which was undertaken in April 2009, was to demonstrate the feasibility of using the HD video technology developed by HiDef Aerial Surveying Limited to:
- survey the larger zones identified in the Round 3 process;
- identify the different species expected in the offshore areas;
- provide confidence to developers, regulators and interested parties that HD video techniques were effective.

It was concluded that the majority of data produced from the survey were of high quality (Hexter, 2009c). However, as with boat-based surveys, there were problems with high levels

A study off the North Wales coast demonstrated the feasibility of using HD video to survey for sensitive species such as the red-throated diver (here shown in summer plumage). © Ómar Runólfsson

Understanding the Environmental Impacts of Offshore Windfarms

of sunlight reflectance from the water when transects were flown towards the Sun on certain bearings. This was not thought to affect the quality of the output but increased the effort required to review and analyse the data.

Aerial surveys of Round 3, Zone 5 for waterbirds

This survey by WWT Consulting, which was undertaken between February and April 2009, collected visual aerial survey data for waterbirds and seabirds over Round 3, Zone 5 to the east of the Norfolk coast (WWT Consulting, 2009). The zone was divided into seven roughly equal-sized blocks to allow maximum coverage on each survey day and, where possible, adjacent blocks were surveyed synchronously to minimise double counting. The data were collected to permit distance analysis and plotting of locations of individual observations.

The survey found that the area covered by the survey supported a diverse range of waterbirds including 3% of Britain's overwintering red-throated diver population. The report's authors expressed caution when comparing data collected during the April surveys with data from the earlier months due to migration of wintering birds away from UK waters from late March onwards and the influx of summer-breeding species such as terns.

Remote techniques

In recognition of the limitations of aerial and boat-based survey methods for documenting bird distributions and movements in periods of darkness or poor visibility and under inclement weather conditions, COWRIE commissioned work to review and develop guidance for the use of remote techniques – principally radar, thermal imaging cameras and individual tracking devices. In particular, the proposed expansion of offshore wind energy development

at increasing distances from the coast poses significant challenges for studying bird interactions with wind turbines – not least because of the health and safety considerations for personnel working offshore.

Development of best practice guidance

The first COWRIE report on remote techniques offered best practice guidance on their use in relation to offshore windfarms (Desholm et al., 2004). The report reviewed technologies that could provide broad pre-construction information on movements of birds and input data for collision risk models. A further report aimed to provide clear and practical guidance on best practice application of remote techniques following experiences in Rounds 1 and 2 (Walls et al., 2009).

The 2004 report reviewed the technical aspects and applications in some detail, primarily for radar and thermal cameras or thermal animal detection systems (TADS). The 2009 report provided a more comprehensive review of the strengths, weaknesses and technical constraints of different remote techniques. Its revised best practice guidance reinforced the need to apply the appropriate technique to address specific questions and provided more practical direction on when and how to apply remote technologies encompassing radar, thermal cameras and tracking techniques. Importantly, the report also considered analytical methods.

The COWRIE guidance on remote techniques highlights the following points.
- Ground truthing or calibration is essential for all techniques.
- Radar is best suited to collecting data on relative numbers and patterns of bird movement (an overview of the different types of radar systems is given in the COWRIE guidance). Calibration of radar requires, among other things, supplementary observations from trained

field observers to check species identification. Clutter from waves or rain interferes with the radar's detection of birds, and the COWRIE guidance includes advice on methods for reducing clutter.

- Thermal cameras use the heat radiating from birds to create a thermal image. The 2009 guidance recommends limiting operational distance to 1–2 km in view of the low optical resolution of thermal cameras, and the need for systems to be robust to operate in the harsh offshore environment.
- Both radar and thermal cameras are capable of streaming huge quantities of data, necessitating good data management and processing systems, and automated routines to increase the efficiency of data extraction.
- The 2009 guidance describes a variety of methods for tagging and tracking of individual birds including radio tracking, satellite tracking, GPS tracking and global location sensing (GLS). The authors stress the importance of selecting techniques appropriate for the study species, including ensuring that the recommended tag to bird mass ratio is not exceeded.

The 2009 guidance also contains a Best Practice Guidance Framework, which incorporates a 'traffic light system' for appropriate remote techniques for ornithological monitoring (Figure 7.2).

Case studies from different offshore windfarm developments including Beatrice (DOWNVInD), Lynn and Inner Dowsing (L-ID), Gwynt y Môr and Sheringham Shoal are featured in the 2009 guidance, presenting lessons learned from the work to date. Table 7.2 provides an overview of the strengths and weaknesses of the various data collection methods.

Limitations in remote techniques include:
- the availability of equipment and suppliers;
- ensuring that suitably qualified and experienced personnel are used.

Figure 7.2 'Traffic light' system for appropriate remote techniques for ornithological monitoring (Walls et al., 2009).

	Radar: land-based	Radar: platform-based	Radar: boat-based	Thermal cameras	Radio tracking	Satellite tracking
Swan sp.	M	M	M	M		M
Goose sp.	M	M	M	M		M
Duck sp.	M	M	M	M		M
Seaduck sp.	W & B	W & B		W & B	?	?
Diver sp.	W & B			W & B	?	?
Auk sp.	W & B	W & B		W & B	B	
Gannet	W & B	W & B	W & B	W & B	B	B
Tern sp.	B	B		B	B	
Skua sp.	W & B	W & B	W & B	W & B	B	B
Shearwaters	B & M			B	B	?
Petrel sp.				B		
Wader sp.	M	M	M	M		?
Passerine sp.	M	M	M	M		
Raptor sp.	M	M	M	M		M

Clear advantages of integrating remote techniques	Possible application of remote technique	Inappropriate technique for species group	M = Migration/passage	W = Overwinter	B = Breeding	? = Unclear in the UK

Table 7.2 Strengths and weaknesses of remote techniques for monitoring birds (Walls *et al.*, 2009).

Technique	Strengths	Weaknesses
Strengths and weaknesses common to all radar systems (unless otherwise stated in specific section)	1. Data can be collected during night time and during periods of poor visibility 2. Objective data collection possible with reduced observer time required from ornithologists 3. Data collection over large area 4. Data collection over long period	1. Susceptibility to adverse wind conditions (wave clutter) 2. Susceptibility to rain (more so X–Band than S–Band) 3. Species discrimination very limited 4. Flock size discrimination very limited 5. Expensive to deploy during pre-construction with limited offshore infrastructure
Ship-based radar	1. Can be deployed for pre-construction monitoring 2. Cheaper and more flexible than permanent systems 3. Multiple and flexible radar positioning possible	1. Requires high level of manual input (acetates) to find and record birds 2. Very susceptible to wave clutter and adverse weather conditions 3. Only records a small percentage of birds present 4. Poor data quality in contrast to platform and land-based radar monitoring 5. Only vertical radar providing good quality data
Long-range radar	1. Can be used for pre-construction monitoring 2. Systems already in place 3. Large detection range 4. Strategic approach to monitoring mass movements	1. Unproven technology in UK 2. Curvature of Earth effects mean low altitude detection unavailable, especially at distance 3. Limited use on a site-specific basis at low altitude particularly for STWR and R3
Military tracking radar	1. 'Species' identification possible 2. Quantitative passage rates can be measured 3. Movements of single birds	1. Very expensive 2. Little scope for remote deployment at sea 3. Not suitable for observing movements over a large area 4. No UK suppliers currently and limited European suppliers 5. Security issues from MOD / DE
Thermal cameras	1. Night time and low-visibility monitoring 2. Species-specific I.D. possible 3. Observations of avoidance behaviour possible 4. Proven application in Danish studies	1. Expensive to deploy 2. Limited detection range dependent on species size Image Intensification – Night Vision 1. Night time and low-visibility monitoring 2. Species-specific I.D. possible 3. Cheaper
Image Intensification – Night Vision	1. Night time and low-visibility monitoring 2. Species-specific I.D. possible 3. Cheaper per unit than thermal cameras	1. Limited detection range dependent on species size 2. Ambient light requirements 3. Poor quality images in contrast to thermal cameras
Radio tracking	1. Ability to monitor movements over long distance (with multiple detectors), and confirm movements from colony or roost to sea 2. Preconstruction use possible if boat-based detector used 3. Individual based modelling information	1. Requires two observers (or boats) to track an individual bird – mass movement data not possible 2. May not produce definitive or representative information because of small sample size. 3. Access to colony or roost may be difficult 4. Licensing requirements to fit tags from BTO
Satellite tracking	1. Ability to monitor movements over long distance without observers 2. Data on long-distance movements available 3. Data downloaded via ARGOS, so no need to re-catch bird 4. Solar-powered units extend the time period over which movements can be tracked, e.g. return migrations	1. More expensive than radio/tracking 2. Tags are heavier than radio/tags, limiting the number of species they can be used on 3. Positional accuracy can be low (4 km at best) 4. May reveal limited info if tag fails 5. Poor weather conditions can affect data recording for tags with solar-powered elements 6. BTO licence requires specialist researchers
GPS tracking	1. Positional accuracy high (±15 m)	1. Must re-catch bird to retrieve logger and data 2. Bird must weigh minimum 1,500 g to carry tag 3. BTO license requirements require specialist researchers
Satellite-linked GPS	1. Combines high resolution of GPS tracking with convenience of data download from satellite	1. Increased tag mass 2. Expensive per unit
Global location sensing	1. Ability to monitor movements over large areas and long time periods (up to two years) 2. Very small and inexpensive	1. Resolution of fixes is low (186 km) 2. No data without sunset/sunrise (e.g. in Arctic winter or summer) 3. Must re-catch bird to retrieve logger and data
Alternative remote techniques largely unproven for ornithological monitoring for offshore environments and in particular windfarms		
Laser range-finders	1. Accurate altitude data possible (for development of collision risk models)	1. Effective range quite limited for birds (up to approximately 50 m) 2. Difficult to measure large quantities of birds
Stereo flock/ filming	1. Detailed information on flock structure and interactions with turbines possible (for development of collision risk models)	1. Equipment cumbersome 2. Requires large degree of manual input for data analysis 3. Unproven offshore
Acoustic monitoring	1. May be the only way to confirm collisions (vibration monitoring) 2. Species discrimination possible	1. Not suitable for boat deployment (presence of boat may effect birds within range of detector) 2. Requires very large amount of specialist analysis 3. Noise contamination offshore

The nature of the work means that remote techniques are often costly. However, the information collected could be crucial to obtaining an accurate impact assessment.

The revised guidance stresses the importance of using all remote techniques as part of an integrated ornithological monitoring programme. It sets out a step-by-step approach which emphasises that:

- remote techniques are not applicable in all cases;
- clear goals must be scoped, stated and agreed before the assessment process starts;
- the aim should be standardised outputs and conclusions;
- remote techniques should be used to provide complementary information to standard ornithological monitoring techniques.

Impact assessment methods: guidance and development

Establishing bird distribution and abundance is just the beginning – the impact of any potential

Visual aerial survey data were analysed to determine whether survey designs were sufficient to allow for detection of changes in bird numbers over and above the natural variation in numbers. © Gareth Bradbury

windfarm must be then assessed. An assessment of the environmental effects of offshore windfarms (including those on birds) requires careful consideration of individual projects alone and in combination with others to highlight impacts of potential significance. COWRIE commissioned a number of reports to address key topics regarding impact assessment, namely:

- investigating the statistical power to detect change in bird numbers;
- examining the process of cumulative impact assessment;
- reviewing the feasibility of conducting population modelling to predict windfarm-induced changes in a bird population.

Power to detect change in bird numbers – aerial surveys

Aerial surveys are increasingly employed as a method for monitoring bird populations in the offshore environment. During the development of a windfarm, a survey's aims are twofold:

- to collect baseline data on birds in the region pre-construction in order to conduct an informed impact assessment;
- if construction goes ahead, to monitor populations to detect any changes in bird distributions and abundance.

Use of aerial surveys to detect bird displacement at offshore windfarms

Although COWRIE had produced guidance on monitoring birds using aerial surveys, it recognised the need to examine this topic in more detail and commissioned two studies, led by the BTO, to investigate whether the existing guidance was sufficient to allow statistically robust detection of changes in bird numbers over and above the natural variation in numbers (Maclean *et al.*, 2006, 2007a). Both studies aimed to provide a statistical assessment of the probability that any windfarm-induced changes in bird numbers could be distinguished from background variation using the survey design current at the time.

The two studies used existing visual aerial survey data. Power analyses (a technique to determine the statistical power in a survey) were performed to assess whether visual aerial survey methods could be used to detect changes in bird numbers given that there are large background fluctuations in seabird numbers at any given site. A further objective was to investigate various ways in which the statistical power (i.e. the probability of detecting a specified change in numbers, in this case a change in bird numbers due to the construction of an offshore windfarm) of surveys could be improved, and make recommendations to achieve this for future work.

Power analyses were conducted by using existing data to generate a series of random datasets with the same mathematical characteristics as the real data. A specified change (e.g. 25% decline) was simulated in each random dataset. These datasets were analysed and the proportion of times that the change was detected at a statistically significant level recorded. This yielded a measure of the 'likelihood of detecting change'.

Four bird species/species combinations were selected for analysis:
- red-throated diver;
- common scoter;
- Sandwich tern (*Sterna sandvicensis*);
- lesser black-backed gull (*Larus fuscus*) and great black-backed gull (*L. marinus*).

The studies differed in that the 2006 study combined data from a number of aerial surveys spread throughout the UK, while the 2007 report utilised a smaller number of longer term, yet geographically restricted datasets (see Figure 7.3).

A number of factors may influence the statistical power of aerial surveys. For each,

Figure 7.3 Location of the three areas from where long time-series of data exist (Maclean *et al.*, 2007a).

Aerial surveys are used to detect any changes in distribution and abundance of bird populations resulting from the construction of offshore windfarms.
© Martin Perrow/ECON Ltd

Table 7.3 Factors influencing the statistical power of aerial surveys.

Factor	Issue	Range	Result	Recommendation
Spatial scale	Can analyse data at a range of spatial scales.	5 x 5 km up to 50 x 50 km	Larger spatial scale = higher probability of detecting change, although when scaled to reflect same decline for different areas, this trend reverses and small grid cells provide highest power. Actual differences are moderate.	Use a spatial scale equivalent to the anticipated windfarm footprint.
Survey intensity	Comparison of conducting surveys only when a given species is abundant (e.g. winter months for red-throated diver) with a year round effort.	Monthly surveys all year versus monthly surveys for six months when birds present.	There is a 3–15% increase in probability of detecting change if surveys conducted all year round.	Extend duration of study to encompass all months when target species occur (if necessary throughout the year).
Survey duration	Differing durations of survey.	2, 3, 4, 5 and 10 years pre- and post-construction.	Power increased moderately with survey duration.	Surveying may not be cost-effective means of increasing power.
Reference area	A reference area is normally used to disentangle windfarm effects from large-scale population changes.	Include 40 and 80 km reference area.	Moderately increases power to detect small changes, decreases power to detect large change.	Make comparisons to a reference area (particularly if relative small changes are predicted).
Effects of mean and peak counts	Power may differ depending on the number of birds present.	Various.	Higher abundance increases power.	Most important determinant of statistical power is mean number.
Covariates	Incorporating meteorological, topographical and hydrodynamic covariates may increase the likelihood of detecting changes.	Bathymetry, distance to land, distance to shallow water, north slope aspect, east slope aspect, seabed complexity.	Including covariates in models lowers variance to mean ratio, however model limitations prevent power calculation. Suggests that oceanographical covariates explain much spatial variance in bird numbers.	Incorporation of static covariates explains much of the variation; including hydrodynamic variables would be expected to explain even more.
Distance bands	Number of distance bands may improve detection (current survey protocols advise using three).	Three versus 10 bands.	No significant increases to the estimated detection probabilities (and hence the bird number estimation) were obtained by increased number of bands.	Carry out ongoing assessment of data collected, with view to improve estimation.
Gradient of decline	Declines in bird numbers are likely to be non-uniform, declining most closest to the windfarm.	Narrow (decline changes rapidly from windfarm) and broad (decline changes slowly).	Overall power appears slightly lower if gradient assumed; this effect is more pronounced for narrow declines. The opposite was true for the common scoter.	Gradients of decline are better accounted for by increasing the spatial resolution of the analysis.
Spatial oceanographic variables (2007)	Including oceanographic variables may help explain variation in count data.	Bathymetry, distance to land, distance to shallow water, north slope aspect, east slope aspect, seabed complexity.	Variables appeared to account for some variation in bird numbers. Incorporating them did not significantly improve power, though in some instances, moderate improvements were calculated (particularly for common scoter). Model constraints make conclusions hard to draw.	Incorporating these variables does not increase power to adequate levels and cannot be used to account for temporal variation in numbers (the primary determinant of statistical power).

statistical models were designed to simulate three different scenarios (declines in bird numbers of 50%, 25% and 10%) and the likelihood of detecting a defined decline in bird numbers was estimated. The results are summarised in Table 7.3.

Conclusions

Overall the statistical power of being able to detect changes in bird numbers is lower than desirable – primarily because of the large inter-annual fluctuations in numbers. Although increasing the frequency or duration of aerial surveys provides one means of increasing the likelihood of detecting changes in bird numbers, the main recommendation on how to improve power is to attempt to account for this temporal variation – potentially by incorporating dynamic oceanic covariates in the analysis. Future work investigating the effect of including hydrodynamic covariate data in analyses of bird numbers would be informative.

Cumulative impact assessment

Cumulative impact assessment (CIA) (i.e. the assessment of impacts associated with multiple windfarm installations or offshore windfarms in combination with other development types) presents considerable challenges.

With the increase in offshore windfarm developments, the need to assess the combined impact of developments on birdlife was recognised. Cumulative impact assessment is also a key component of environmental impact assessment, alongside the assessment of the in-combination effects of plans or projects on features of European sites, i.e. the interest features of Special Protection Areas (SPAs) and Special Areas of Conservation (SACs). The absence of guidance for carrying out cumulative impact assessment was a notable gap and one which led to generally poor consideration of cumulative impact assessment in EIAs.

COWRIE workshop on cumulative impact of offshore windfarms on birds

In 2007 COWRIE contracted RPS to convene a workshop attended by representatives from 36 organisations to discuss this subject and to develop recommendations to inform future CIAs (Norman *et al.*, 2007). This workshop identified the challenges surrounding the assessment of cumulative effects on birds in the offshore environment, and the need for written guidance to assist in the process of assessing the cumulative impacts of windfarms on birds. Delegates agreed that this guidance should:
* be based on scientific principles;
* recommend methodologies robust enough to meet statutory requirements;

Cumulative impact assessment considers the impacts associated with multiple windfarm installations or offshore windfarms in combination with other development types.
© Dan Towers 2004. RWE npower renewables North Hoyle Offshore Wind

- be practicable for developers to carry out within the timeframes and resources normally available for environmental impact assessment.

Developing guidance on ornithological CIA for offshore windfarm developers

COWRIE subsequently commissioned a consortium consisting of BTO, AMEC and PMSS to develop guidance based on these three key aims. The guidance (King *et al.*, 2009) covered:
- the regulatory issues concerning CIA;
- the methodological requirements;
- the cumulative impacts to be assessed.

To inform the production of this guidance, a position paper was commissioned to consider the regulatory context of CIA. This paper identified three key processes:
- **Scoping.** A standardised approach to scoping would provide consistency across and between projects, and would define parameters for early discussion. A 'key features' document could accompany a scoping request and form the basis for subsequent discussions. The benefits of utilising a 'key features' document include early data acquisition and fuller engagement with stakeholders. This increased emphasis on early and informed scoping could entail greater 'front end' costs for the developer.
- **Pre/post application communication.** Communication between the regulators, statutory advisors, stakeholders, developers and consultants should be improved, as the failure of all parties to fully address cumulative impacts at an early stage has been a barrier to progression. The need for regular and frequent meetings, and transparent and open exchange of information, was stressed.
- **Policy and guidance.** There is a need for policy and guidance to provide context, as

COWRIE guidelines recommend that CIA consider wide-ranging SPA species, such as the gannet (pictured). © Martin Perrow/ECON

developers and consultants have to some extent been working in an uncertain regulatory environment where the approach to cumulative impact assessment has tended to be ad hoc and on a case-by-case basis. Clear guidance on EIA would assist in providing greater certainty as to the approach taken by the agencies when balancing the environmental impacts of offshore wind (including cumulative impacts) against the climate change and biodiversity benefits of renewable energy.

A second position paper considered the methodological aspects of CIA and made the following recommendations:

- **Species selection.** Because cumulative assessment of all species at a site would be unmanageable, a 'long list' of species to be considered in the CIA should be drawn up at the scoping stage and then screened. These species are:
  - all local SPA species (taking account of whether wide-ranging SPA species such as gannet are present);
  - species of conservation importance (e.g. Annex I of the Birds Directive);
  - species whose population within the study area exceeds 1% of the national population;
  - species thought to be at particular risk from windfarms.
- **Project selection.** The following projects should fall within the scope of a CIA:
  - projects that have been consented but yet to be constructed;
  - projects for which application has been made;
  - projects that are reasonably foreseeable;
  - non-windfarm projects subject to EIA;
  - existing projects yet to exert a predicted effect (i.e. an effect not covered in the baseline).
- **Which population and which reference area?** The selection of the area and

population for consideration is extremely significant when conducting a CIA, particularly if modelling techniques are to be used to assess potential impacts.

- For SPA species, the reference population to be used is that cited in the SPA.
- For non-SPA species or those whose 'home' SPA cannot be assigned, best available expert judgement should be used to define the area and regional population.
- The default boundary of the CIA study area for defining regional populations should be considered as the relevant Round 2 strategic area, Round 3 zone or equivalent unless there is reliable evidence to support the definition of an alternative discrete biogeographical region.
- Depending on the reference population(s) identified, impacts may need to be considered at different population scales at different times of year.

Windfarms may act as barriers to birds, such as these migrating pink-footed geese. © Martin Perrow/ECon Ltd

- **Methods of data gathering.** In the past, data to inform cumulative assessments have been those collected for the purposes of an environmental impact assessment. In general it was agreed that the standards specified for EIA data collection was adequate for CIA.
  - Data should be collected using standard methods (e.g. according to Camphuysen *et al.*, 2004) by trained/experienced observers. New recommendations or refinements should be taken into account (e.g. Maclean *et al.*, 2009).
  - In general, CIA should be based on data gathered for EIA and not require the collection of additional data except in special circumstances.
  - Where additional data gathering is required, it should be agreed with stakeholders as early as possible, and preferably at the scoping stage.
  - For Round 3 zones and other adjacent projects, data gathering should be standardised as far as possible across projects.
- **Data analysis.** The analysis of cumulative impacts often involves combining datasets from a number of different projects, which can lead to compatibility problems. The following recommendations were made to address this issue:
  - Raw bird numbers (including survey dates), density estimates and population estimates should be reported for all species together with a description of their methods of calculation.
  - All data analysis should be presented in as clear a way as possible, identifying any parameters used and assumptions made.
  - In the long term, a system of standardised results reporting for Environmental Statements should be developed to ensure compatible outputs.

Cumulative effects

The potential **impacts** of windfarms on birds, all of which may act cumulatively, include:
- disturbance;
- displacement;
- barrier effects;
- mortality due to collisions;
- indirect effects on prey.

Table 7.4 summarises these effects and how they should be addressed in a cumulative impact assessment.

Table 7.4 Effect and cumulative impact assessment summary.

Impact	Description	Treatment in CIA		Notes
		Low impact	Significant impact	
Collision	Mortality via collision with turbines	Quantitative summed	Quantitative summed	Further population modelling may be required
Disturbance	Birds disturbed from area – effectively leads to habitat loss	Qualitative	Quantitative non-linear	Energy budgets may need to be modelled/calculated
Displacement	Displacement from windfarm results in habitat loss	Qualitative	Quantitative summed	Areas are presumed to be at carrying capacity; the default assumption is that displacement equals mortality
Barrier effects	Windfarms may act as barriers to birds – altering their flight paths and increasing their energy requirements	Quantitative summed	Quantitative non-linear	Assessment of flight directions, bird origin and energetics may be required
Indirect effects	For example, disturbance to prey species	Unknown	Unknown	Lack of information on the subject – but should be considered

Assessing the significance of a cumulative impact is a complex process. The following recommendations were made concerning **tests of significance**:

- In general, the significance of mortality should be expressed by presenting the number of individuals as a proportion of the population. It should also be interpreted as a change in background mortality to enable the life history parameters and ecology of the species to be taken into account.

- Consideration of cumulative impacts should be given not only to those species for which there is a significant impact at any one of the component developments, but should also include species that narrowly miss this category.

- The significance of cumulative impacts should be initially assessed using the same matrix approach as that routinely used for EIA. This should be supported by detailed discussion of the predicted impact to substantiate the conclusion of a significant or non-significant effect.

- The results of both EIA and CIA should be presented in the Environmental Statement in as clear a way as possible, identifying any parameters used and assumptions made. The preference should always be for results to be quantitative rather than qualitative.

Conclusions

The COWRIE guidance covers the processes, methods and techniques to be utilised for cumulative impact assessment for birds and offshore windfarms. It was agreed that the process of scoping is essential to the provision of robust CIA. The need for improved communication and provision of clearer guidelines was also identified.

The review of the methods and techniques currently used for CIA led to two main areas of recommendation. The first focused on data gathering and analysis; guidelines are given for selection of species for consideration, the projects to be included in the assessment and the spatial scale of the bird reference population to be used. The second concerned assessment of cumulative effects; recommendations on how to address the different impacts and how to calculate the significance of predicted mortality were made.

The guidelines are the first stage of an iterative process. They will need to be refined on the basis of evidence gathered from the monitoring of windfarms both during and post-construction and as our understanding of the impacts of cumulative effects on birds improves.

Population viability analysis: feasibility study

In any population, death is a fact of life. The impact of mortality rates on a population is influenced by a host of other intrinsic (birth rate, life span) and extrinsic (predation, habitat loss) factors. Although it can be calculated that a windfarm is likely to cause mortality to a certain number of individuals, the implications of this mortality to the bird population under consideration differs widely depending on these other factors. The impact of windfarm-induced mortality therefore needs to be assessed at a population scale rather than at the scale of the individual.

Population modelling can be used to help evaluate the consequences of changes in mortality rates on population growth and viability. Population viability analysis (PVA) is a specific branch of population modelling. It is used extensively in conservation biology and is concerned with predicting the future viability of a population under a range of differing ecological scenarios.

PVA can be a useful tool in assessing the impact of a windfarm on a given bird population. A model can be constructed to reflect the specific species (and population) in question, incorporating vital statistics such as adult survival and reproductive success, stochastic events (e.g. random variation in population growth between seasons) and even catastrophes (e.g. fox predation at a seabird colony). Scenarios can then be designed to model the effects of a windfarm (or several windfarms) on this population, and predict what effect these will have on population viability. However, the robustness and hence predictive ability of PVA is defined by the quality of the estimates used (e.g. adult survival) to inform the model.

Potential use of PVA to assess the impact of offshore windfarms on bird populations

Recognising that the effectiveness of PVA as an impact assessment tool depended largely on the data available, COWRIE commissioned a study from the BTO to assess whether sufficient data existed for the relevant species of waterbirds and seabirds to build PVAs that would have value as an impact assessment tool in the offshore environment (Maclean *et al.*, 2007b). The report discussed the following topics:

- **Species considered most vulnerable to collision risk.** Based on the vulnerability index devised by Garthe and Hüppop (2004) and expert opinion, 25 species were identified for inclusion in the report (Table 7.5).
- **Key parameters.** The researchers assessed which parameters were of importance for these species to inform a PVA. Both individual demographic parameters and factors that affect these such as resource availability and predation were judged to be significant when building a PVA model (see Table 7.5 for summary list of parameters).
- **Data gathering.** A literature review was conducted using a scientific search engine and manual searching to ascertain whether

data existed to provide estimates for these parameters. Emphasis was placed on studies conducted on UK populations, but data from studies elsewhere were also included.

- **Scoring of data.** The data availability per species was summarised and the data scored depending on their quality and importance as a parameter in the model. As scoring was a product of data availability and importance, the resulting assessment for each species (Excellent, Good, Reasonable and Poor) indicated the suitability of conducting a PVA given existing data (see Table 7.5).
- **Software.** The PVA software currently available was reviewed and recommendations made regarding which to use; the report compared the capabilities of five of the most widely used software packages (GAPPS, INMAT, RAMAS, VORTEX, and ULM).

Much of the demographic data needed to inform a basic population viability analysis are generally available and thus a population viability approach to determining the impact of offshore windfarms on seabird populations should be possible. Use of the software package ULM was recommended as this allows the most sophisticated means of incorporating age- and density-dependent differences in demographic factors. Of the 25 species assessed in the study, 15 scored as 'reasonable' or above in terms of data quality (three scored 'excellent' and four scored 'good') (Table 7.5).

Conclusions

There are sufficient data to suggest a PVA approach could be used to assess the extent to which direct mortality from collisions with wind turbines affects populations. However, the approach has some limitations and the indirect impacts of this mortality are harder to assess. For example, adult mortality could result in reduced competition for food resources (potentially leading to an increase in adult survival); conversely, displacement of birds from windfarm areas into less suitable areas could lead to an associated increase in mortality via resource competition.

Another critical issue in determining the impact of windfarms on bird populations is the question of migration between populations, and what exactly constitutes a population as opposed to say one colony which forms part of a larger population. To determine the overall

Table 7.5 Demographic data availability (mean and variance) for species likely to be vulnerable to offshore windfarms (Maclean et al., 2007b).

	Adult survival	Productivity	Age-dependent survival	Age-dependent productivity	Incidences of non-breeding	Migration between meta-populations	Density-dependent survival	Density-dependent productivity	Score
Red-throated diver	Y	Y	N	N	N	N	N	N	16
Black-throated diver	Y	Y	N	S	N	N	N	N	16
Great crested grebe	Y	N	N	N	N	N	N	N	6
Fulmar	Y	Y	Y	Y	N	S	N	N	26
Gannet	Y	Y	S	N	N	N	N	N	18
Cormorant	Y	Y	Y	Y	Y	Y	Y	N	42
Shag	Y	Y	Y	Y	N	Y	Y	N	34
Eider	Y	Y	N	S	Y	S	N	Y	30
Common scoter	Y	Y	S	N	N	N	N	N	18
Velvet scoter	Y	Y	S	N	N	N	N	N	17
Arctic skua	Y	Y	N	Y	Y	N	N	N	28
Great skua	Y	Y	N	Y	Y	N	S	N	35
Little gull	S	N	N	N	N	N	N	N	4
Black-headed gull	Y	Y	Y	Y	N	S	N	N	26
Common gull	Y	Y	N	Y	N	N	N	N	20
Lesser black-backed gull	Y	Y	N	Y	N	N	N	N	24
Herring gull	Y	Y	N	Y	S	S	N	Y	26
Great black-backed gull	Y	Y	N	N	N	N	N	N	14
Kittiwake	Y	Y	Y	Y	Y	Y	Y	Y	46
Sandwich tern	Y	Y	N	N	N	N	N	N	14
Arctic tern	Y	Y	Y	N	N	N	N	N	20
Little tern	N	Y	N	N	N	N	N	N	8
Guillemot	Y	Y	Y	Y	Y	Y	N	Y	40
Razorbill	Y	Y	Y	N	S	N	N	N	26
Puffin	Y	Y	Y	N	S	S	S	Y	37

Y = Good information available; S = Some information; N = No information. ■ = Excellent score; ▨ = Good score; ☐ = Reasonable score; ☐ = Poor score. A score had been calculated for each species to indicate the overall quality of data available. The score is the product of a data availability score (Yes = 2, Some = 1, No = 0) and a score which indicates the likely importance of each of the demographic components for carrying out population viability analysis, judged by expert opinion (5 = very important to 0 = no importance). Thus, a high score indicates good data availability. The maximum score that can be attained is 46.

impact on one population it is necessary to identify the extent of interchange with neighbouring populations, as a potential reduction in one localised population could be compensated for if sufficient migration from other populations occurs.

Despite the difficulties associated with determining the indirect effects of offshore windfarms on bird populations, PVAs nevertheless provide a useful framework in which such issues can be explored. Even without precise parameter values, reasonable estimates can be incorporated into PVA models and the sensitivity of results to variations in these values assessed. This has the dual advantage of enabling the range of likely impacts on bird populations to be determined in terms of worst-case or best-case scenarios, but also allows an assessment of what the greatest uncertainties are in terms of determining the impact of windfarms on bird populations. This in turn will allow more focused future research related to offshore windfarms.

The COWRIE report (Maclean et al., 2007b) provides a valuable reference on which species are suitable for impact assessment via PVA and highlights the gaps in data availability that could be addressed.

Research on specific bird species

As well as providing guidance on survey techniques and impact assessment methodologies, COWRIE commissioned specific studies on several bird species that posed particular concerns in relation to offshore windfarm development. The common scoter, whooper swan (*Cygnus cygnus*) and several species of terns were the focus of three research projects.

Common scoter habitat displacement

The UK breeding population of common scoter is small and occurs on inland freshwater sites in Scotland and Ireland. In winter, UK waters are host to thousands of common scoter thought to comprise local breeding birds and migrants from breeding grounds in Scandinavia and Iceland, but probably augmented by birds from further afield during late summer when they

UK waters are host to thousands of common scoter, a diving duck known to be susceptible to disturbance, especially from boat traffic. © Martin Perrow/ECON Ltd

moult their flight feathers and grow new ones. The common scoter is a diving duck that feeds on benthic organisms such as bivalve molluscs attached to rocks or living in the sediments on the seabed. The species is noted for being susceptible to disturbance, especially from boat traffic, and in particular during moult when they are less adept at flying and tend to aggregate on the sea in 'rafts' of up to several thousand birds.

Studies in Denmark at the Horns Rev I offshore windfarm found that common scoters showed almost complete avoidance of the area encompassing the windfarm and a 4 km buffer in the first three years post-construction. Subsequent aerial surveys indicate that the birds may now be utilising the sea areas within the windfarm in comparable densities to those outside the windfarm area (Petersen and Fox, 2007).

Concerns relating to the likelihood of disturbance (leading to displacement from foraging areas) prompted COWRIE to commission a project to model the response of common scoter to several different scenarios of wind energy development in Liverpool Bay

COWRIE - BEN - 03 - 2002
Predicting the displacement of common scoter
Melanitta nigra from benthic feeding areas due to
offshore windfarms

COWRIE commissioned a project to model the response of common scoter to several different scenarios of wind energy development in Liverpool Bay.

(Kaiser *et al.*, 2002). The collaboration between the University of Wales Bangor, the Centre for Ecology and Hydrology (CEH) and the University of East Anglia developed an individual-based behavioural model for common scoter to explore possible effects on overwinter survival of different wind development scenarios in Liverpool Bay. The project's objectives were to:
- develop a computer simulation model to assist in predicting the effect of offshore windfarms (individually and cumulatively) on common scoter due to habitat loss and change;
- link the non-breeding distribution of common scoter with environmental variables at selected sites;
- identify the characteristics of preferred feeding areas for common scoter within these sites (including a description of density, species and size classes of prey).

The study entailed the collection of field data from Liverpool Bay including visual aerial surveys of common scoter, benthic sampling to record prey species, behavioural observations of scoters and their response to disturbance, and quantification of disturbance sources. These data were augmented by data from the published literature on common scoter or closely related species.

The purpose of the behavioural model was to predict the change in overwinter mortality of the common scoter population of Liverpool Bay that might result from the displacement of birds from feeding grounds in close proximity to offshore windfarms, based on the assumption that common scoter will avoid using areas of sea either within an array of turbines or within a wider area around such arrays. The model was based on fundamental ecological principles such as maximising individual survival, which will apply under any environmental conditions. It predicts how each individual bird in the population would redistribute its foraging effort in space and time in response to environmental change, and whether or not these behavioural responses would enable them to survive the winter. The combination of survival consequences for each individual enables the model to generate the predicted population-level mortality.

The model was used to simulate a variety of combinations of, at the time, existing (North Hoyle), consented (Rhyl Flats and Burbo Bank), and proposed (Gwynt-y-Môr and Shell Flat) windfarms. Additional simulations explored the consequences of removing what appeared in the model to be the most profitable feeding areas within Liverpool Bay, as well as testing the sensitivity of model outputs to variation in its key input variables.

Study findings

Common scoter were found within water depths of 2–22 metres in Liverpool Bay, but concentrated in depths of 10–12 metres, with bird densities dropping steeply in depths of 18 metres or more. The tidal state affects the availability of suitable water depths for scoters. The highest numbers of common scoter observed during visual aerial surveys coincided with sites that had a high abundance and biomass of bivalve mollusc prey species.

Observations from a 35-metre long vessel revealed the presence of a critical flushing distance of approximately 1 km, at which flock size increased quite dramatically. Large flocks of common scoter were put to flight at a distance of 2 km or more from the vessel, while smaller flocks (≤15 birds) permitted closer approach before flushing at a distance of 1 km. Larger vessels would be expected to lead to a larger flushing distance.

More than 100 scientific papers and reports concerning the physiology, diet, energetics, foraging ecology and general behaviour of diving ducks were collated for the literature review in order to:

- build up knowledge of the way in which diving ducks forage;
- derive reasonable assumptions on which the behavioural model could be based;
- obtain values for the many parameters needed by the model;
- identify independent empirical data against which model outputs could be validated.

Most of the information sourced from the literature review did not relate specifically to common scoter, reflecting the inaccessible nature of the habitat in which the birds live during the winter months. Although not ideal, it was therefore necessary to include information relating to other species of diving duck.

When running the model, the only scenario that predicted a significant adverse effect on survival of common scoter was their displacement from areas of the sea up to 2 km beyond the footprints of the windfarms at Rhyl Flats, Burbo Bank, Gwynt-y-Môr and Shell Flat, in addition to that at North Hoyle.

Under this scenario, the median mortality of common scoter increased to 11.7% (range 11–12.2%) compared with the baseline condition (Liverpool Bay with North Hoyle) of a median mortality of 7.3% (range 5.5–8.8%). The predicted increase in common scoter mortality was due to the presence of a windfarm on Shell Flat, in combination with the other windfarms. This reflects the fact that, only in those scenarios which included a 2 km buffer zone around the Shell Flat windfarm, did the model predict that common scoter would be excluded from areas in which it was expected they would otherwise feed heavily.

This cumulative adverse effect of multiple windfarms may be negated if:
- the radius of the buffer zone is smaller than 2 km (but note the Horns Rev I study findings of displacement from a larger area);
- common scoter redistribute to currently unused but apparently profitable feeding areas within Liverpool Bay; or

- common scoter feed during the hours of darkness as well as during daylight.

Conclusions

Behavioural models such as that developed for common scoter in Liverpool Bay have a useful role in testing the potential effects of different development scenarios. The approach is data-intensive and caution is needed in interpreting models that rely on data from other species (albeit closely related), necessitating model validation.

Whooper swan migration: collision v barriers

Swans are long-lived and noted for their large body size and low manoeuvrability, necessitating a long distance to take off from land or water, hence the particular concern about their potential for collision with wind turbines. Whooper swans breeding in Iceland overwinter in the UK, notably in northwest England and the fenland hinterland to the Wash Estuary in eastern England. COWRIE commissioned The Wildfowl and Wetlands Trust (WWT) to carry out a tracking study of whooper swans. The project (Griffin *et al.*, 2010) entailed fitting satellite tags to known individuals at various wintering locations in mainland Britain in winter 2008–2009 and to birds on their Icelandic breeding grounds during summer 2009. The project's objectives were to:

- determine the migration routes and flight heights of whooper swans between their breeding grounds in Iceland and the UK in relation to offshore windfarms, particularly in the eastern Irish Sea and Greater Wash strategic areas;
- publish the results on a website to provide up-to-date information on the whooper swans' migration routes and flight heights, and to provide easy access to all interested parties including the public;
- assess the potential impacts of weather during migration (particularly periods of poor or adverse conditions);
- determine the potential risk to whooper swans from offshore windfarms.

Whooper swan at The Wildfowl and Wetlands Trust centre at Martin Mere, Cumbria. © Kane Bride

Whooper swan fitted with satellite tag in flight.
© David Hickson

Forty GPS satellite transmitters were fitted to whooper swans in winter 2008–2009 (20 at WWT Martin Mere in northwest England, 15 at WWT Welney in southeast England and five at WWT Caerlaverock in southwest Scotland) to follow birds during their northbound, spring migration to Iceland. A further 10 transmitters were fitted and one transmitter redeployed in Iceland in August 2009 to provide information about the swans' southbound tracks during autumn migration.

To conserve battery life and maximise data collection when swans were most likely to pass through or near to the footprints of offshore windfarms, the transmitters were programmed to provide hourly positions of the birds during the main migration period. The transmitters indicated whether or not a bird was moving (e.g. flying or roosting) when its position was recorded.

Swan location data were downloaded from the ARGOS satellite monitoring system (www.argos-system.com) together with weather data from UK meteorological weather stations, and imported into a geographical information system (GIS). Data on the swans' migration patterns (i.e. timing, altitude and direction of flight) at specific locations were extracted for analysis in relation to the weather data that most closely matched the swans' locations (derived from the satellite fixes) in time and space. Computer models were used to determine which environmental variables had a significant influence on the whooper swans' migration.

Swan round-up in Iceland. © Eileen Rees

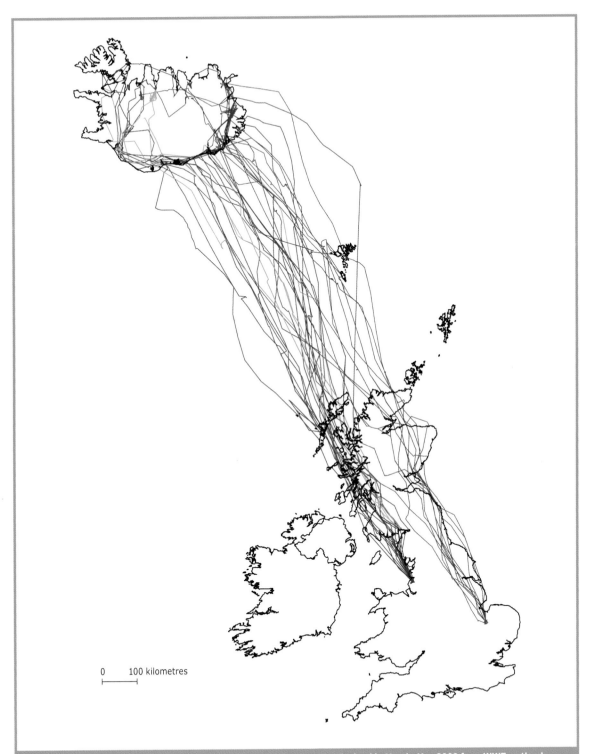

Figure 7.4 Migration routes of 35 whooper swans tracked from the UK to Iceland in March–May 2009 from WWT wetland centres (Griffin et al., 2010). Swans from Welney are shown by red lines, those from Martin Mere by blue lines and those from Caerlaverock by green lines. Tracks for four birds that remained in the UK and one for a Martin Mere ringed bird whose tag was removed at Caerlaverock are not shown.

Study findings

Of the 40 whooper swans tagged in winter 2008–2009, 35 (88%) were tracked to Iceland in spring 2009. Peak spring migration occurred in mid to late March. Once the birds had left the UK coast for Iceland, the 800 km (500 mile) sea crossing was completed in less than three days with two Welney birds completing the flight in just eight hours at speeds of 90–100 km/hour.

Once migration had begun, the swans' decision to stop or to continue on their migration was influenced significantly by light conditions, wind direction, atmospheric pressure, and the interaction of wind speed and direction. The swans were significantly less likely to continue their migration in moonlight or in darkness than in daylight, and were more likely to continue migration with side winds or particularly tailwinds than in headwinds. There was also a significant positive association between onward migration and atmospheric pressure.

Swans migrating from eastern England (Welney) generally migrated north along the east coast of Britain, whereas those from northwest England and southwest Scotland (Martin Mere and Caerlaverock) followed the western coastline (Figure 7.4). Nineteen whooper swans from Martin Mere, crossing Liverpool Bay and the Solway Firth, passed through or within 5 km of existing or proposed Round 1 and Round 2 windfarms (Figure 7.5), whereas none were recorded passing through or within 5 km of the proposed Scottish territorial waters sites close to Islay, Tiree or Kintyre.

Of the 15 swans tagged at Welney, no birds flew within 30 km of any of the Round 3 zones in the Greater Wash area. It is also unlikely that any of the flight paths crossed existing or proposed Round 1 or Round 2 sites, although one came to within 4 km. Most tracks of birds from Welney passed through the Firth of Forth and Moray Firth Round 3 sites; only one flew across a proposed Scottish territorial waters site.

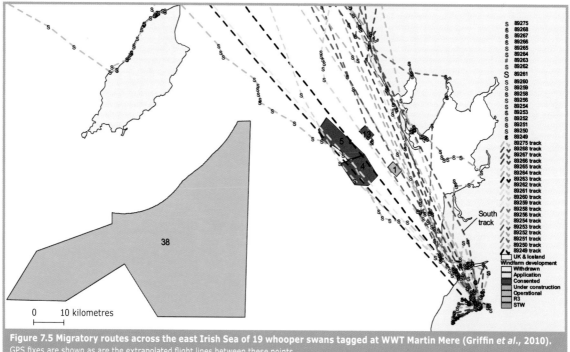

Figure 7.5 Migratory routes across the east Irish Sea of 19 whooper swans tagged at WWT Martin Mere (Griffin *et al.*, 2010). GPS fixes are shown as are the extrapolated flight lines between these points.

On average, swan flights were lower over the sea when crossing from Britain to Iceland than when they were migrating along the coast of Britain. Most flights through west coast offshore windfarms were in tailwinds. The flights through Liverpool Bay and the Solway Firth occurred equally during daylight and darkness, the latter often without the aid of moonlight.

The median flight elevation was below 20 metres across Liverpool Bay and the Solway Firth, with over 90% of flights below 50 metres and over 60% below 20 metres (Figure 7.6). However, the median flight elevation increased to 100 metres when crossing the North Channel, with 43% at or below 50 metres and 29% at or below 20 metres. This was probably because of the juxtaposition in this region between high land and narrow sea channels.

Two notable exceptions may provide evidence of avoidance of offshore windfarms. Two swans recorded flight heights of 172 metres and 160 metres at 8.9 km and 3.8 km north of Barrow (operational) and Robin Rigg (near operational) respectively. The flight heights of these birds one hour previously had been 40 metres above land of height around three metres and 55 metres above land of height around 10 metres respectively. The Barrow crossing was at dawn, whereas the Robin Rigg crossing was at night under moonlit and possibly cloudy conditions. The report's authors suggested that radar studies on the Solway during the period covering the first week of

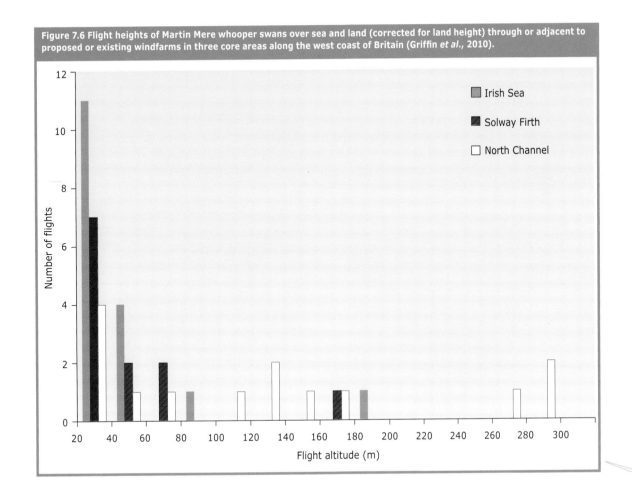

Figure 7.6 Flight heights of Martin Mere whooper swans over sea and land (corrected for land height) through or adjacent to proposed or existing windfarms in three core areas along the west coast of Britain (Griffin et al., 2010).

March to the first week of April would add useful information.

The sample of swans on their southbound, autumn migration from Iceland comprised just eight tracks, but despite the very small sample sizes, it seems that the swans were more likely to pass across proposed windfarm sites in Scottish territorial waters and to traverse a series of these sites in succession.

'Super Whooper' website

The 'Super Whooper' website (www.wwt.org.uk/whooper) described the project and provided live updates of maps showing the swans' movements. There were 16,535 unique visits to the site recorded between its launch on 10 March 2009 and February 2010. Peak numbers of visits to the site coincided with the swans' migration period and also with media coverage such as the BBC's SpringWatch series in late March–early April 2009. Nine of the satellite-tagged swans were followed closely by local schools – three each at Caerlaverock, Martin Mere and Welney.

Conclusions

Spring migration of whooper swans along the west coast of Britain tended to be over coastal waters, bringing migrating whooper swans into or close to the footprints of several existing or proposed offshore windfarms, with flights occurring below or within the rotor swept area and so potentially at risk of collision. For two birds (one in daylight and one in moonlit conditions), there is a possibility that they avoided the wind turbines by increasing their flight elevation. Spring migration along the east coast of Britain tended to be close to the coast or over land, with few birds passing within or near the footprints of offshore windfarms and thus indicating little risk to the swans. The small autumn sample of tracks indicated that migrating swans were more likely to pass through or close to several windfarms in succession.

These results are based on just one spring and one autumn migration, and so may or may not be representative of the migratory routes taken by whooper swans each year. Nonetheless, tracking studies such as this add to our understanding and permit evaluation of the risk to birds arising from windfarms that may intercept their flight routes. The public profile of this project illustrates the potential for people engagement and education.

Homepage of the WWT 'Super Whooper' website (9 March 2010).

Breeding terns: foraging range and collision risk

Five species of terns occur in the UK as breeding birds and, to varying degrees, during migration. Breeding Sandwich terns, common terns (*Sterna hirundo*) and little terns (*Sternula albifrons*) have all featured as species of potential concern in relation to proposed offshore windfarms in the Greater Wash; collision or indirect effects on foraging habitat are the main concerns.

The breeding colony of Sandwich terns at Scolt Head/Blakeney Point forms part of the North Norfolk Coast SPA and accounts for 5–6% of the European breeding population of this species. Aerial and boat-based surveys on their own are inadequate for determining areas of important foraging habitat for terns in relation to proposed windfarm footprints.

The COWRIE tern study sought to build on study techniques developed by the environmental consultancy, ECON, as part of its work in the Greater Wash strategic area (on behalf of AMEC/Centrica) to permit more rigorous assessment of the risks for terns posed by offshore windfarms (Perrow *et al.*, 2010). The project's main objectives were to:

- further the understanding of the foraging ecology (including range and behaviour) of several tern species;
- provide data for modelling foraging distribution and collision risk (where specific windfarm sites exist).

Fieldwork was undertaken during 2008 and 2009. In 2008 the study focused on 26 Sandwich terns and 42 common terns in the Greater Wash during the late stages of the breeding season (July). In 2009 the study was extended to several

Common tern. © Martin Perrow/ECon Ltd

Sandwich terns resting near the Scroby Sands windfarm. © Martin Perrow/ECon Ltd

Sandwich tern. © Martin Perrow/ECon Ltd

Understanding the Environmental Impacts of Offshore Windfarms

other sites to test the wider applicability of the approach throughout the breeding season (May to August). The 2009 studies were of:

- 138 Sandwich terns from the Ynys Feurig, Cemlyn Bay and The Skerries SPA on Anglesey in North Wales;
- seven Arctic terns (*Sterna paradisaea*) from the same SPA;
- 107 common terns from RSPB Saltholme on Teesside in northeast England.

The methods deployed combined a number of study techniques:

- visual tracking of terns into and out of breeding colonies from a high-powered, rigid-hulled inflatable boat (RIB);
- a combination of observations at colonies and boat-based colony transects (immediately offshore from the colony) to estimate flight bearing and passage rate of outbound and inbound birds;
- development of an individual-based computer simulation model to determine foraging patterns of birds (derived from flight bearing and distance relationships);
- detailed observations of the type and rate of provisions delivered to chicks;
- development of an energetic model to predict the optimality of different provisioning strategies, including how far adults could travel from breeding colonies;
- use of data collected by visual tracking in collision risk modelling.

The individual-based model was used to generate predictions of the relative importance of different areas including offshore windfarm areas, and the number of passages by birds across those areas in the course of a breeding season. The modelled proportion of birds foraging in particular areas, including offshore windfarms, was compared with the real but coarse distribution generated by tracking birds and from aerial surveys carried out according to the protocol published by the then Department of Trade and Industry (DTI) in 2006 (DTI, 2006). Birds overflying any area (including an offshore windfarm) on the way to another, more distant foraging endpoint could also be determined.

Tracking birds at sea and recording flight patterns (flight height, foraging behaviours, interaction with other species, etc.) and prey selection (number, type and size of prey consumed or transported), together with observations of prey delivered to chicks, provided detailed information on feeding and breeding ecology – essential for assessing the potential impact of offshore windfarms.

Little tern fitted with radio tag. © Martin Perrow/ECon Ltd

Rigid-hulled inflatable boat used to track Sandwich and common terns in 2008, with driver and recorder (the observer is taking the picture). © EMU Ltd

Study findings

Visual tracking of terns from a boat was found to be an effective study technique for most foraging trips, although there were limitations in quantifying the extent of longer distance movements offshore. A high degree of species- and site-specificity was observed in prey selection, foraging patterns and behaviours – all relevant to the birds' risk profile in relation to offshore windfarms.

In the Greater Wash, common terns specialised in small prey items including invertebrates and fish such as young clupeids, selecting the latter as the main food for chicks. A high feeding rate was maintained with birds foraging at low flight heights (often less than one metre above the sea surface), using surface feeding in particular. The feeding rate for

Tracked Sandwich tern emerging from a plunge-dive with a small (~6 cm) sandeel. © Martin Perrow/ECon Ltd

Common tern presenting two small (~4 cm) clupeids (a single item is more usual) to its chicks. © Martin Perrow/ECon Ltd

Sandwich terns was significantly lower because they fed by plunge diving from height. Clupeids and sandeels were typically caught; the larger size of these items compensated for low feeding rates, meaning the rate of prey biomass ingested/captured did not differ significantly between Sandwich and common terns.

Although common terns were simply able to present transported prey to chicks, Sandwich terns suffered kleptoparasitism (prey-stealing) by black-headed gulls (*Chroicocephalus ridibundus*) at their shared colony. The intensity and frequency of kleptoparasitism was sufficient to influence chick provisions, which were dominated by small clupeids as they were for common terns. However in order to maintain chick growth, Sandwich terns had to succeed in delivering some larger prey items in the course of each day.

In the Greater Wash, the maximum distance (Figure 7.7) reached by the 42 tracked common terns in 2008 was just 2 km offshore, though birds did travel up to about 9 km from the colony parallel with the coast. In contrast, common terns at Teesside were observed to forage over greater distances (up to 18 km in 2009) and take larger prey, indicating a different risk profile for common terns at a different location. In contrast, Sandwich terns in the Greater Wash reached 22 km offshore in 2008 though earlier studies had indicated foraging ranges extending to at least 53 km. The shorter distance registered in July 2008 was probably attributable to terns making shorter foraging trips to provision chicks later in the season.

Visual tracking registered 7.7% of Sandwich tern flights within or through offshore windfarms, compared with 3.4% predicted by

Successful kleptoparasitism by a black-headed gull upon a Sandwich tern with a large sandeel. The tern was brought down in the process and pinned to the ground by several attacking gulls. © Martin Perrow/ECon Ltd

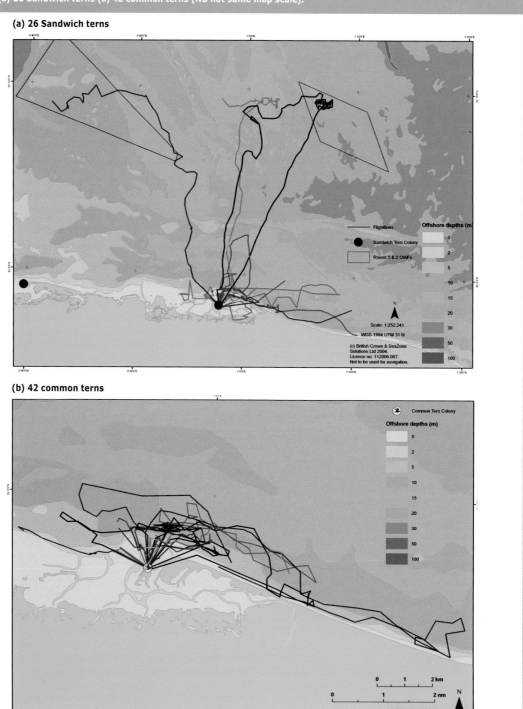

(a) 26 Sandwich terns

(b) 42 common terns

the individual-based model. However, the model indicated that the same two offshore windfarm sites visited by tracked birds were the most likely to be selected, accounting for 95% of simulated endpoints/flyovers within an offshore windfarm.

A key factor in collision risk is the flight height of birds passing through offshore windfarms. In the Greater Wash, foraging Sandwich terns spent significantly more time at a greater flight height than common terns, 49% of time above 20 metres compared with 6.7% for common terns, and compared with similar overall distribution of flight height categories (Figure 7.8). Observations of tracked birds yielded a substantially higher percentage of flight time within the collision risk height than obtained from boat-based survey snapshots.

Collision risk modelling for Sandwich terns (based on limited data for the latter part of the 2008 breeding season) indicated a low collision risk, invariably linked to the tendency for shorter flights during chick provisioning. However, application of the collision risk model for common terns at Teesside indicated significant additive mortality.

The energetic model indicated that Sandwich terns are energetically capable of freely ranging across the area encompassed by the Round 2 Greater Wash strategic area (Figure 7.9) – unless prey abundance declines or kleptoparasitism becomes too intense. Therefore a better understanding of the importance of different areas relative to offshore windfarms is essential.

Taking into account all modelling scenarios as well as recorded ranges for different tern species, the report suggests the following guide values for range: Sandwich tern ≤75 km and common tern approximately 18 km (in line with other sources). The limited evidence for one Arctic tern, tracked for 57 km at up to 29 km from the Skerries colony before being lost, yields a higher value than previously recorded and indicates that the Round 3 Irish Sea Zone is within flight range.

Conclusions

This study indicates that vulnerability to offshore windfarms appears to be highly site- and species- specific as illustrated by the differences between the Sandwich and

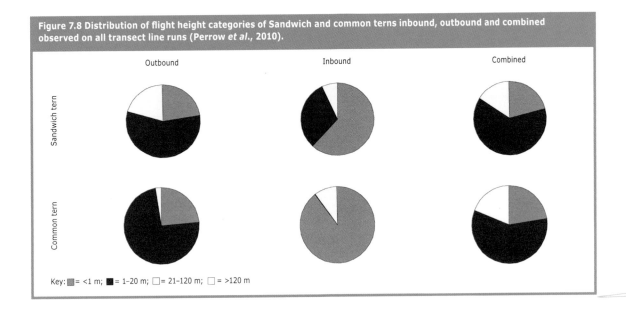

Figure 7.8 Distribution of flight height categories of Sandwich and common terns inbound, outbound and combined observed on all transect line runs (Perrow *et al.*, 2010).

Key: ■ = <1 m; ■ = 1–20 m; □ = 21–120 m; □ = >120 m

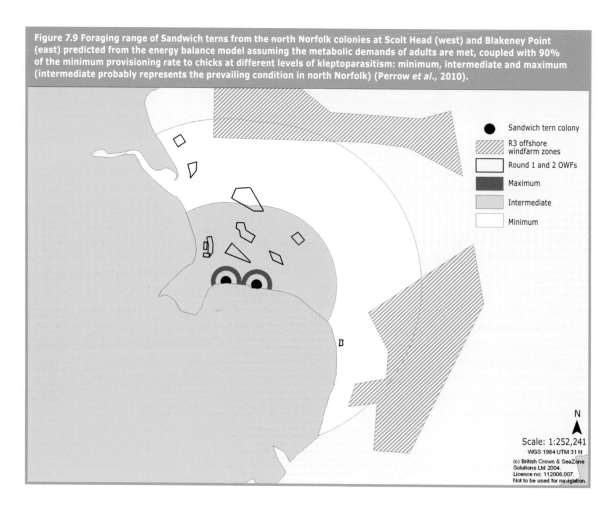

Figure 7.9 Foraging range of Sandwich terns from the north Norfolk colonies at Scolt Head (west) and Blakeney Point (east) predicted from the energy balance model assuming the metabolic demands of adults are met, coupled with 90% of the minimum provisioning rate to chicks at different levels of kleptoparasitism: minimum, intermediate and maximum (intermediate probably represents the prevailing condition in north Norfolk) (Perrow et al., 2010).

common tern observed in the Greater Wash, and the differences for common tern between the Greater Wash and Teesside. This highlights the need for targeted studies at individual sites. The study demonstrates the value of the approaches used and makes recommendations for their application in studies before and after construction of offshore windfarms, as well as their potentially wider adoption for some other species of seabird.

Overall conclusions

COWRIE has been instrumental in the development of survey techniques and impact assessment methodologies, and in furthering research into specific species issues. Some of the key conclusions from its 20 reports on bird-related topics are summarised below.

- The value of all survey effort is greatly increased by ensuring statistical compatibility of the data collected. Collecting data using recognised standard methodologies gives confidence to developers, regulators and interested parties that the information supplied within an environmental impact assessment or a Strategic Environmental Assessment is of value and a representative record of the use of offshore windfarm areas by birds. It is essential that surveys and targeted studies are designed to address the key questions for the species of interest. This remains work in progress, necessitating periodic revision of guidance as new techniques and evidence emerge.

- The guidance produced by COWRIE on cumulative and other impact assessment is the first stage of an iterative process which should continue during the development of offshore windfarms. It is vital to refine impact assessment methods as evidence is gathered through the standardised surveys (as recommended by COWRIE) together with other studies.

- Models provide useful tools in the assessment of environmental impacts. However, models are only as good as the information used to create them. Information from post-construction monitoring of offshore windfarms needs to be used to validate and further develop modelling approaches.

- Alongside furthering our understanding of potential impacts from offshore windfarms, it is also necessary to increase our understanding of natural change and variability in bird populations.

Perhaps the greatest achievement of COWRIE is in bringing together regulators, developers, nature conservation agencies and non-government organisations to discuss and move forward the assessment of the potential impacts of offshore windfarms on birds. Discussing complex issues of concern was not without its difficulties, and even though the issues raised often took some time to resolve, without the regular meetings of the Environment Technical Working Group and Birds Subgroup it is unlikely that the exchange of information and views enabled by these fora would have taken place.

References

Band, W. 2000. *Windfarms and birds: calculating a theoretical collision risk assuming no avoidance action*. Scottish Natural Heritage, Inverness.

Burt, L., Rexstad, E. and Buckland, S. 2009. *Comparison of visual and digital aerial survey results of avian abundance for Round 3, Norfolk Region*. COWRIE Report STANDBIRD-09. Report prepared for COWRIE by the Centre for Research into Ecological and Environmental Modelling, University of St Andrews. COWRIE Limited, London.

Camphuysen, C.J., Fox, A.D., Leopold, M.F. and Petersen, I.K. 2004. *Towards standardised seabirds at sea census techniques in connection with environmental impact assessments for offshore windfarms in the UK*. COWRIE Report BAM-02-2002. Report prepared for COWRIE by Royal Netherlands Institute for Sea Research. COWRIE Limited, London.

Department of Trade and Industry (DTI). 2006. *Aerial surveys of water birds in strategic windfarm areas: 2004/05 Final report*. DTI/Pub 8298/0.7k/05/06/NP. DTI, London.

Desholm, M., Fox, A.D. and Beasley, P.D. 2004. *Best practice guidance for the use of remote techniques for observing bird behaviour in relation to offshore windfarms*. COWRIE Report REMOTE-05-2004. Report prepared for COWRIE by National Environmental Research Institute (NERI) and QinetiQ. COWRIE, London.

Garthe, S. and Hüppop, O. 2004. Scaling possible adverse effects of marine windfarms on seabirds, developing and applying a vulnerability index. *Journal of Applied Ecology* 41: 724–734.

Griffin, L., Rees, E. and Hughes, B. 2010. *The migration of whooper swans in relation to offshore windfarms*. COWRIE Report SWAN-06-08. Report prepared for COWRIE by The Wildfowl & Wetlands Trust. COWRIE Limited, London.

Hexter, R. 2009a. *High resolution video survey of seabirds and mammals in the Moray Firth, Hastings, West Isle of Wight and Bristol*

Channel Areas in Periods 5, 6 and 7 2009. Technical report. COWRIE Report HIDEF-07-00. Report prepared for COWRIE by HiDef Aerial Surveying Limited. COWRIE Limited, London.

Hexter, R. 2009b. *High resolution surveys of seabirds and mammals in the Rhyl Flats Area.* COWRIE Report RTD-01-09. Report prepared for COWRIE by HiDef Aerial Surveying Limited. COWRIE Limited, London.

Hexter, R. 2009c. *High resolution surveys of seabirds and mammals in the Norfolk Area.* COWRIE Report ZONE-01-09. Report prepared for COWRIE by HiDef Aerial Surveying Limited. COWRIE Limited, London.

Kaiser, M.J., Elliott, A., Galanidi, M., Rees, E.I.S., Caldow, R., Stillman, R., Sutherland, W. and Showler, D. 2002. *Predicting the displacement of common scoter* Melanitta nigra *from benthic feeding areas due to offshore windfarms.* COWRIE Report BEN-03-2002. COWRIE, London.

King, S., Maclean, I., Norman, T. and Prior, A. 2009. *Developing guidance on ornithological cumulative impact assessment for offshore wind farm developers.* COWRIE Report CIBIRD. Report prepared for COWRIE by the British Trust for Ornithology, AMEC and PMSS. COWRIE Limited, London.

Maclean, I.M.D., Skov, H., Rehfish, M.M. and Piper, W. 2006. *Use of aerial surveys to detect bird displacement by offshore windfarms.* COWRIE Report DISP-03-2006. BTO Research Report No. 446. Report prepared for COWRIE by the British Trust for Ornithology, DHI Water and Environment, and biola. COWRIE Limited, London.

Maclean, I.M.D., Skov, H., and Rehfish, M.M. 2007a. *Further use of aerial surveys to detect bird displacement by offshore windfarms.* COWRIE Report EXTDISP-06-07. BTO Research Report No. 482. Report prepared for COWRIE by the British Trust for Ornithology, DHI Water and Environment, and biola. COWRIE Limited, London.

Maclean, I.M.D., Frederiksen, M. and Rehfisch, M.M. 2007b. *Potential use of population viability analysis to assess the impact of offshore windfarms on bird populations.* COWRIE Report PVA-03-07. BTO Research Report No. 480. Report prepared for COWRIE by the British Trust for Ornithology and the Centre for Ecology & Hydrology. COWRIE Limited, London.

Maclean, I.M.D., Wright, L.J., Showler, D.A. and Rehfisch, M. M. 2009. *A review of assessment methodologies for offshore windfarms.* COWRIE Report Meth-08-08. Report prepared for COWRIE by the British Trust for Ornithology. COWRIE Limited, London [updated version issued 2010].

Mellor, M., Craig, T., Baillie, D. and Woolaghan, P. 2007. *Trial high definition video survey of seabirds.* COWRIE Report HIDEF-05-07. Report prepared for COWRIE by HiDef Aerial Surveying Limited. COWRIE Limited, London.

Mellor, M. and Maher, M. 2008. *Full scale trial of high definition video survey for offshore windfarm sites.* COWRIE Report HIDEF-03-08. Report prepared for COWRIE by HiDef Aerial Surveying Limited. COWRIE Limited, London.

Perrow, M.R., Gilroy, J.J., Skeate, E.R. and Mackenzie, A. 2010. *Quantifying the relative use of coastal waters by breeding terns: towards effective tools for planning & assessing the ornithological impact of offshore windfarms.* COWRIE Report TERN-07-08. Report prepared for COWRIE by ECON Ecological Consultancy Ltd. COWRIE Limited, London.

Petersen, I.K. and Fox, A.D. 2007. *Changes in bird habitat utilisation around the Horns Rev 1 offshore windfarm, with particular emphasis on Common Scoter.* Report prepared for Vattenfall A/S by National Environmental Research Institute (NERI), University of Aarhus, Denmark. Vattenfall A/S, Copenhagen.

Norman, T., Buisson, R. and Askew, N. 2007. *COWRIE workshop on the cumulative impact of offshore windfarms on birds: Peterborough, 3rd May 2007.* COWRIE Report CIBIRD-01-2007. Report prepared for COWRIE by RPS. COWRIE Limited, London.

Thaxter, C.B. and Burton, N.H.K. 2009. *High definition imagery for surveying seabirds and marine mammals: a review of recent trials and development of protocols.* COWRIE Report BTO-Workshop-09. Report prepared for COWRIE by the British Trust for Ornithology. COWRIE Limited, London.

Walls, C., Pendlebury, C., Budgey, R., Brookes, K. and Thompson, P. 2009. *Revised best practice guidance for the use of remote techniques for ornithological monitoring at offshore windfarms.* COWRIE Report REMTECH-08-08. Report prepared for COWRIE by RPS, Food and Environment Research Agency (FERA) and the University of Aberdeen. COWRIE Limited, London.

Webb, A. 2010. *Joint Nature Conservation Committee Seabirds at Sea team. Computer coding manual* (7th edition). JNCC, Peterborough (www.jncc.gov.uk/pdf/SAS_SAST_Coding_Manual_v7.pdf).

WWT Consulting. 2009. *Aerial surveys of Round 3, Zone 5 for waterbirds – final report.* COWRIE Report ASURV-02-09. Report prepared for COWRIE by WWT Consulting. COWRIE Limited, London.

8 Marine data and information management

Chris Hill

The COWRIE Data Management System containing the extensive information submitted by offshore windfarm developers plus the data gathered during COWRIE research projects will remain accessible to all through an online portal hosted by The Crown Estate

DATA MANAGEMENT for the marine and coastal zone has been rising up the agenda as new marine activities and new approaches to resource allocation and planning have emerged. The advent of marine renewables has extended the detailed surveys of a wide range of environmental factors to new areas around the UK coastline, generating ever larger volumes of data and information.

COWRIE's Data Technical Working Group set up the main data management programme to create and maintain a system for windfarm developers to submit data into an online metadata, data and information repository. This portal (http://data.offshorewind.co.uk) is now hosted by The Crown Estate to ensure that COWRIE's Data Management System is accessible to everyone into the future.

A number of other projects initiated by the Data Technical Working Group examined various aspects of data management of relevance to the wind renewables community. The data and reports from these and all the other projects funded by COWRIE are also accessible via the data management website.

Background to marine data management in the UK

Offshore wind site investigations, environmental assessment and monitoring, and ongoing operations and management all have a high demand for primary survey and secondary data. This is equally true of many other sector operations in the marine and coastal zone for planning, allocation and management of resources where access to data and information is an important first step in planning and evaluating options. The volumes of data generated have increased as the levels of offshore activity have risen, and as survey techniques evolve and data storage and processing capacity expand.

There is growing concern and appreciation that the huge investment in marine data collection should not be lost by ineffective management that prevents discovery and access to data for other purposes. The motivation to 'collect once, use many' is an important driver for the offshore sector where the physical challenges and costs of survey

Navigational information on survey vessels: marine data collection and management requires accurate locational information and logbook records for subsequent data use. © English Heritage

work are large and where project delays may be significant if relevant data are not available from which to make environmental or technical assessments. Within such environments, data collected by offshore developers supplement the often sparse baseline information.

This growing realisation of the value of datasets is evident in the public sector where legislation and policies exist to improve both access to and reuse of public sector information. In addition, the Infrastructure for Spatial Information in Europe (INSPIRE) Directive and the UK Location Programme (UKLP) provide the framework for the development of the UK Spatial Data Infrastructure (UKSDI). Equally, new marine organisations such as the Marine Management Organisation (MMO) – and new procedures for regulation, planning and habitat protection zones – are likely to increase the demand for

effective access to data and information to assist resource planning, management and regulatory decision support.

Within the marine sector, the Marine Environmental Data and Information Network (MEDIN) provides a framework of co-ordinated yet distributed data archive centres (DACs), web portal and metadata standards to support the marine components of the emerging Marine Spatial Data Infrastructure (MSDI).

The UK's Marine Science Strategy published in February 2010 also emphasises the importance of access to data as a significant element in marine science priorities and in enabling effective collaboration.

Although marine offshore windfarm environmental data sit largely outside these public sector requirements and approaches, COWRIE and The Crown Estate have aligned data management development with the principles of MEDIN to encourage the sharing

Jack-up-rig used during windfarm installation of Thanet. The data management process for offshore windfarms extends beyond the impact assessment and consenting surveys through to installation, monitoring and operational stages. © English Heritage

and effective reuse and stewardship of environmental data.

The COWRIE Data Management System is one of a number of marine data and information management systems for the UK managing thematic or geographic cover of environmental data. Together these provide a wealth of information to support the range of marine activities.

COWRIE data management objectives

Round 2 developers have a duty to submit data and information to The Crown Estate. This obligation does not stop at the point of consent following the environmental impact assessment (for which many environmental datasets are collected), but runs on into licence monitoring requirements and the operation and maintenance phases of the windfarm.

To help developers fulfil this commitment The Crown Estate identified the need for a robust system that allowed the developers themselves to be responsible for:

- their data and information management;
- submitting data and information.

Often within the development project the generation and management of data is divided between the developer partners and contractors. Through the promotion of data and information management plans and an online data management system, the COWRIE data website became the vehicle by which developers discharged their duty to submit data. In line with developer commitments, the website provides a platform for ongoing updates and submission as well as supporting data discovery and downloads.

COWRIE developed an accessible and intuitive system that provided leading data management functions and standardised metadata delivery requirements. It also provided a managed service, supported by the COWRIE data officer to help developers understand data submission requirements.

In establishing COWRIE's data and information management system the primary objective was to:

- make the data collected through the Round 2 programme freely accessible over the Internet to a wider community;
- foster greater use of the data in marine resource management;
- stimulate further studies and research.

A further objective was to make data and information generated during the environmental research projects commissioned by COWRIE accessible to a wider audience through the same online portal.

In addition, the Data Technical Working Group initiated a number of data research projects to address some of the challenges faced by developers in understanding best practice. These projects investigated:

- survey and modelling techniques;
- data standards;
- how best to manage the volumes and types of data generated by site surveys and environmental investigations.

COWRIE Data Management System

Section 5 of the lease agreements between The Crown Estate and the individual tenants for the 15 Round 2 windfarm sites places a duty on the tenants to supply environmental information to The Crown Estate. Submission of such data relies on having somewhere to manage and retrieve the information and so The Crown Estate asked COWRIE to organise a programme to manage the data generated from offshore wind developments.

COWRIE's data management system was designed by the GeoData Institute of the University of Southampton to support developer data submission and to be automated where possible. This allows the commitment for ongoing submission to be fulfilled without continual intervention by COWRIE or The Crown Estate. With lease agreements running over 40–50 years, the long-term data management plan and capability are important components in the system's design and operation.

What data are on the system?

The information submitted by the tenants and their developer partners includes a wide range of raw and processed environmental data. The requirements for submission are set under the lease but, as a starting point, seminars were held with COWRIE, The Crown Estate, developer stakeholders and contractors to agree the scope of data submissions.

In addition to the Round 2 data submissions, a number of other data resources can be accessed through the web portal (Figure 8.1). Although not obliged to submit information, some Round 1 developers recognised the value of the COWRIE Data Management System and

provided some datasets (there is currently less information relating to Round 1 sites). The environmental impact assessments conducted for the Round 1 sites are also available online.

The COWRIE system takes data and information from the assessment, construction and operational stages and potentially, in the longer term, from decommissioning. Data management for long-term use in charting change will give these resources value into the future.

Also submitted to the COWRIE system are data from developers fulfilling part of their reporting under the Food and Environment Protection Act (FEPA) licence terms set by the Marine Management Organisation (MMO) – but again only currently for Round 1 sites. The system also holds the records of data generated from the research programmes supported by other COWRIE Technical Working Groups.

Data and information themes include all the environmental (natural and socio-economic) information collected during site investigations, impact assessment and operation (Figure 8.2). Thus the breadth of data is very large – from

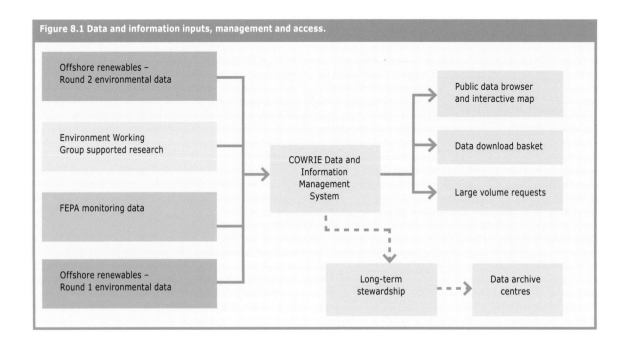

Figure 8.1 Data and information inputs, management and access.

birds to benthos, morphology to marine mammals – and includes wind resource data.

Although the focus of the data within the COWRIE system is marine it also encompasses coastal and terrestrial data from cable connections surveys. In general, the website does not hold technical design and engineering or operational data and information.

The website also hosts a number of other components including:

- Route Map to Offshore Wind Data (see below and Figure 8.10);
- data advice pages;
- guidance and training materials;
- white papers;
- links to environmental impact assessment, policy documents, and data management guidance and standards.

Architecture and interface

COWRIE's data programme consists of an online data management application, backend database, and online and offline data store. A user support service answers queries from data submitters and users, and provides quality assurance of the system.

The web portal is based on standard metadata (data about the data) which allow users to locate and then download data, or for larger datasets, to request them from the data officer. It is usually possible to view reports online. Access to detailed metadata records and the ability to download datasets and reports requires registration and log in.

To support this functionality COWRIE's data management team has developed a

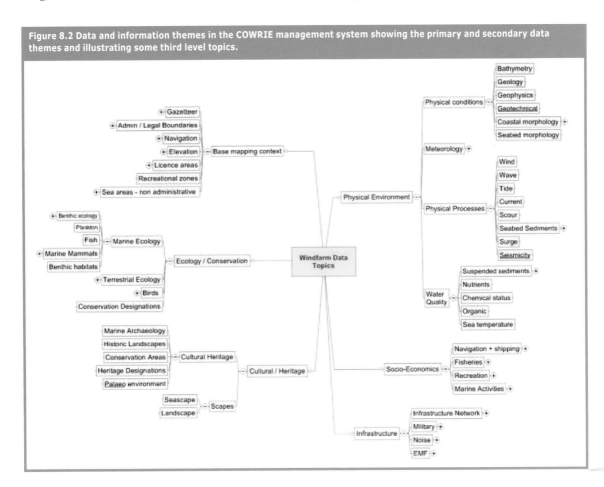

Figure 8.2 Data and information themes in the COWRIE management system showing the primary and secondary data themes and illustrating some third level topics.

sophisticated system built on Open Source software components. These provide an advanced interface (Figure 8.3) to:

- submit and validate metadata entries to international standards;
- upload datasets and textual reports related to a project;
- search and view metadata for projects, datasets and reports;
- administer and manage data, report downloads and supply constraints;
- carry out site management and user administration functions.

Full details on how to submit and access data are given in *Measurement of environmental data and information from offshore renewables* (COWRIE, 2007).

The data structure is based on holding standard metadata for all projects and data plus the reports related to each project. This is supported by a backend database and secure back-up procedures.

Example search

As an example, it is possible to search for all projects, data and reports relating to birds on the Gunfleet Sands windfarm in the Thames Estuary. From the search interface users can search by keyword and/or the site name, or they can use the map interface to refine the area of the search (Figure 8.4).

The returned results are a series of projects, data sources and reports; further filtering of the datasets retrieved is possible. In this example there are five projects with two reports and 15 datasets available.

The search results list a number of datasets that can be selected for download. A basket

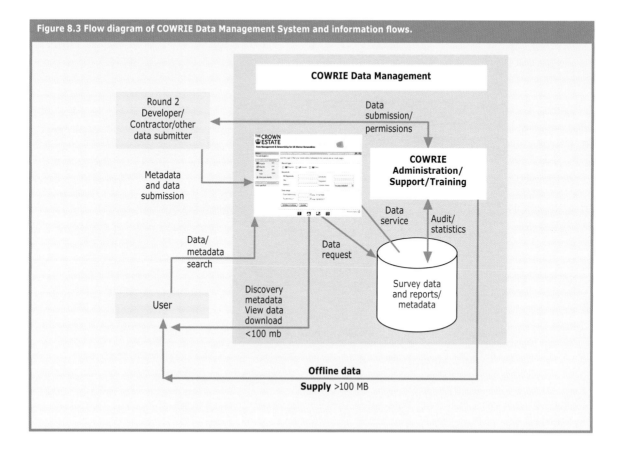

Figure 8.3 Flow diagram of COWRIE Data Management System and information flows.

system allows up to 100 MB of data to be downloaded directly; above this volume users can request copies of data. Clicking on the individual datasets takes you to a summary and the detailed metadata for the individual item; these will help you decide whether you wish to download the dataset.

Having found the datasets the data can be selected for upload to a basket (Figure 8.5). You can check that the files are the right ones by looking at the data and detailed metadata. These provide:

- detailed descriptions of the resource and data attributes;
- information on the data quality and currency;
- any access restrictions that might apply.

Go to the basket download to be sent the files (Figure 8.6) or, if the volumes of data are too large, to request the information be sent to you on a disk.

Training and support

All windfarm developers and a number of survey consultants have sent staff on COWRIE data management training courses. A 'data' newsletter was published by COWRIE in October 2008. Its data management team has also attended the main annual British Wind Energy Association (BWEA; now RenewableUK) events (Figure 8.7 and photo), helping to spread understanding of the commitments and value of the offshore renewables information.

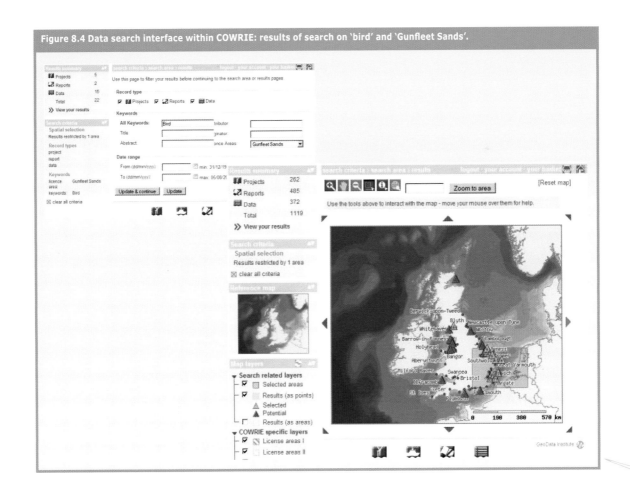

Figure 8.4 Data search interface within COWRIE: results of search on 'bird' and 'Gunfleet Sands'.

Figure 8.5 Selecting and exploring data and information held on the COWRIE system.

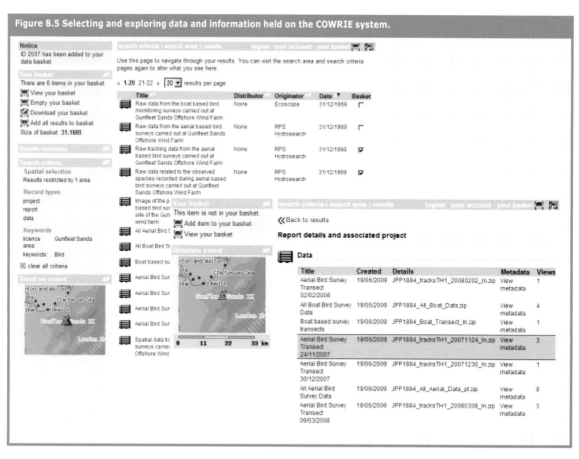

Figure 8.6 COWRIE data download interface.

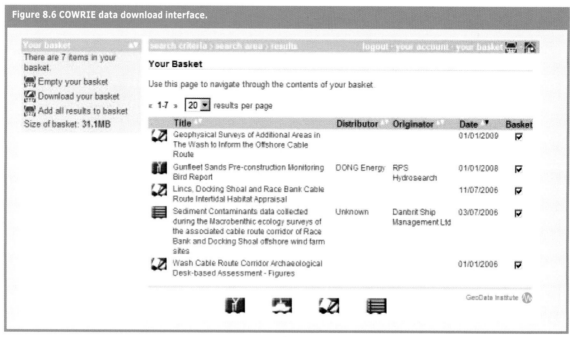

Understanding the Environmental Impacts of Offshore Windfarms

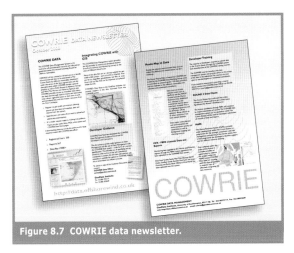

Figure 8.7 COWRIE data newsletter.

The COWRIE data team in attendance at the BWEA national meeting, Glasgow. © GeoData Institute

Website statistics

As of September 2010 the website has 830 registered users, including representatives from all Round 2 developers. The 31 GB of online data are made up of 1,824 reports and 1,542 data files. In addition, there are 1.45 TB of data held offline. The numbers of separate data records and projects for each of the Round 2 sites are shown in Figure 8.8.

Other data programmes

The Data Technical Working Group selected five additional research programmes. Two of these related to coastal process and sediment monitoring and dynamics (see Chapter 3):

- *Coastal process modelling for offshore windfarm environmental impact assessment: best practice guide* (Lampkin *et al.,* 2009);
- *A further review of sediment monitoring data* (Carroll *et al.,* 2010).

The other three projects covered diverse areas:

- development of spatial information layers for commercial fishing and shellfishing in UK waters (ABPmer, 2009);
- data management for marine biological data (Seeley *et al.,* 2009);

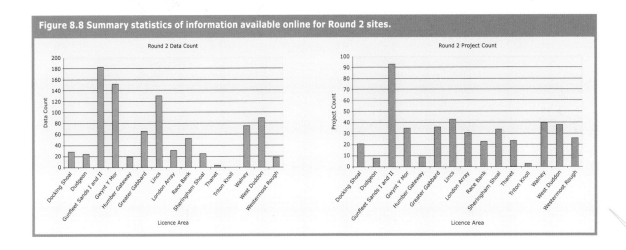

Figure 8.8 Summary statistics of information available online for Round 2 sites.

- sources of geographical and thematic data required for offshore windfarm development (Route Map to Data).

Details of these three projects are given below.

Development of spatial information layers for commercial fishing and shellfishing in UK waters

Geospatial data layers on the distribution and economic value of commercial fishing and shellfishing activities within UK waters were created by ABP Marine Environmental Research Ltd (ABPmer), the Centre for Environment, Fisheries & Aquaculture Science (Cefas) and Fisheries Research Services (FRS). The programme collated vessel monitoring system (VMS) data and non-VMS data to provide a picture of fishing effort from UK waters.

The study aimed to create a series of consistent UK-wide marine information layers and to make these widely available through the COWRIE Data Management System. The final outputs were a series of geospatial data layers displaying the annual mean fish value for 2004–2007 for different types of fishing activity. Two of the outputs are illustrated in Figure 8.9.

These data complement other data layers produced by ABPmer and partners within the Defra Marine Renewables Resource Atlas which have helped renewable developers in resource planning.

The report (ABPmer, 2009) has been widely accessed from the website but there is potential to update the assessment as new records become available to improve the information provided, particularly for inshore areas.

Best practice for the documentation and dissemination of marine biological data

Marine biological data cover a broad spectrum of data types including species, habitat and the environmental characteristics of the areas of study. They also frequently include image and

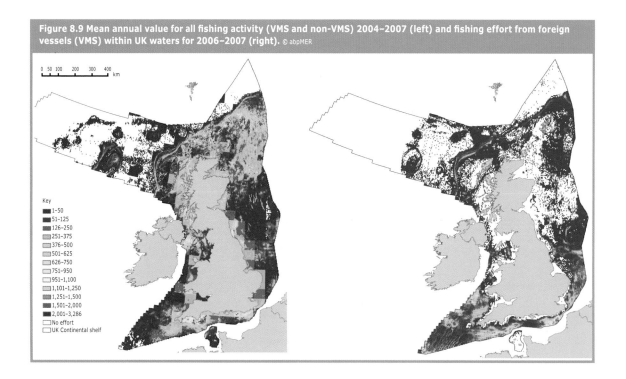

Figure 8.9 Mean annual value for all fishing activity (VMS and non-VMS) 2004–2007 (left) and fishing effort from foreign vessels (VMS) within UK waters for 2006–2007 (right). © abpMER

Key
- 1–50
- 51–125
- 126–250
- 251–375
- 376–500
- 501–625
- 626–750
- 751–950
- 951–1,100
- 1,101–1,250
- 1,251–1,500
- 1,501–2,000
- 2,001–3,286
- No effort
- UK Continental shelf

video datasets. This breadth raises issues of the quality and standardisation of data collection submission.

This study (Seeley *et al.,* 2009) reviewed the approaches to documenting and disseminating marine biological data. Through a series of workshops in 2007, the Marine Biological Association (MBA) and DASSH (Data Archive for Species and Seabed Habitats) brought together groups of stakeholders to examine standards for:

- marine biological data;
- image and video;
- metadata.

The workshop findings and research resulted in the production of best practice guidance in documenting and disseminating marine biological data as a basis for further development and discussion. The aim is to enhance the dissemination and use of marine biological data between contractors and data commissioners, and between data providers and data archive centres, such as DASSH. The study also looked at survey and data protocols, and the key information and metadata required to document methodologies and ensure ongoing usability of data.

Route Map to Data

With the launch of Round 3 in 2007 there was an increasing need to locate new thematic data covering other areas of the seabed.

With all potential applicants looking for relevant spatial information, the COWRIE Data Technical Working Group commissioned the GeoData Institute at the University of Southampton to develop and populate a directory of core spatial data sources. This system was developed rapidly to provide this information and the Route Map to Data is available online (Figure 8.10). This may be a useful source if you want to locate data on physical environment, ecological, socio-economic and cultural heritage themes.

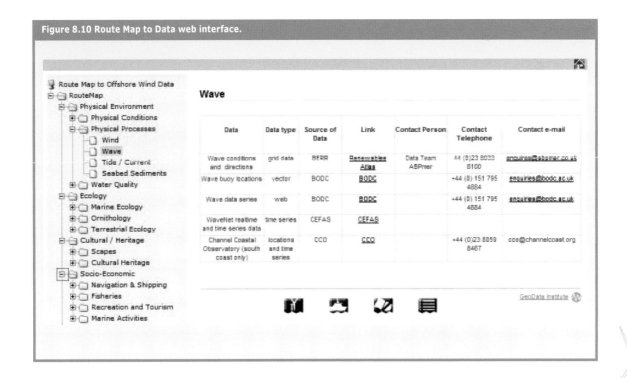

Figure 8.10 Route Map to Data web interface.

Future prospects

The Crown Estate took over the COWRIE data management programme on 1 January 2010. A transition period ensured that, as a legacy of the COWRIE programme, there is an effective mechanism for continued access to metadata and data and support to users. The COWRIE data website – rebranded as 'The Crown Estate Data Management & Stewardship for UK Marine Renewables' – reflects the developer's submission obligations and provides support for longer term management and access to data through stewardship. The interface is likely to change, but the true legacy is the volume of data that the system maintains.

The Crown Estate is also looking at the value of the offshore wind data collated within the COWRIE programme with potential to contribute to understanding the marine resource managed and leased by The Crown Estate. In this sense, the legacy of the COWRIE data management system for The Crown Estate is fundamental environmental data covering part of its marine estate and the waters above. The COWRIE Data Management System is providing rapidly increasing volumes and coverage of environmental data that had been lacking. Although there are extensive areas where there is still no survey information, these data contribute to a greater understanding of the marine environment within and around renewables zones, cable routes and the foreshore.

Looking forward, the Round 3 Zonal Appraisal and Planning (ZAP) process and the requirement for environmental impact assessments and technical engineering plans will also benefit from this collated and managed, accessible information as will other marine industrial sectors (e.g. marine aggregates, other marine renewables, cabling). These will generate even larger volumes of marine and coastal datasets that will need effective management and distribution.

The COWRIE Data Management System is also contributing to The Crown Estate's Marine Resource System (MaRS) – an innovative, multi-criteria based spatial analysis tool designed to help future resource allocation and sustainability assessments.

COWRIE offers a leading source of data on environmental impact studies and marine surveys, assessments and monitoring results. Its ongoing collation by The Crown Estate, through developer data and metadata submissions, should make this an increasingly valuable resource for researchers, developers, regulators and the wider community.

References

ABPmer Ltd, 2009. *Development of spatial information layers for commercial fishing and shellfishing in UK waters to support strategic siting of offshore windfarms*. COWRIE Report FISHVALUE-07-08. Report prepared for COWRIE Limited. COWRIE Limited, London.

Carroll, B., Cooper, B., Dewey, N., Whitehead, P., Dolphin, T., Rees, J., Judd, A., Whitehouse, R.

Data Management & Stewardship for UK Marine Renewables

http://data.offshorewind.co.uk

and Harris, J. 2010. *A further review of sediment monitoring data.* COWRIE Report ScourSed-09. Report prepared for COWRIE by ABPmer with Cefas and H R Wallingford. COWRIE Limited, London.

COWRIE. 2007. *Management of environmental data and information from offshore renewables.* Prepared for COWRIE by GeoData Institute. COWRIE Limited, London.

Lampkin, D.O., Harris, J.M., Cooper, W.S. and Coates, T. 2009. *Coastal process modelling for offshore wind farm environmental impact assessment: best practice guide.* COWRIE Report COAST-07-08. Report prepared for COWRIE by ABPmer Ltd and H R Wallingford. COWRIE Limited, London.

Seeley, B., Parr, J., Evans, J. and Lear, D. 2008. *Establishing best practice for the documentation and dissemination of marine biological data.* COWRIE Report DATA-07-08. Report prepared for COWRIE Ltd by The Marine Biological Association and DASSH (Data Archive for Seabed Species and Habitats). COWRIE Limited, London.

Other documents

Doneghan, G. and Hill, C. 2006. *COWRIE data management system: training manual.* COWRIE Limited, London.

Hill, C. and Sadler, J.D. 2005. *Data and information management plan.* Prepared for COWRIE by GeoData Institute. COWRIE Limited, London.

9 Education and communications

Dr Carolyn Heeps and
Eleanor Partridge

COWRIE has used various methods including
a website, reports, interactive maps,
teaching resources, student awards, events
and conference presentations to increase
knowledge of the potential environmental
impacts and benefits of the UK offshore
windfarm programme

FROM THE outset education and communication has been a core activity for COWRIE Limited to fulfil its aim *'to advance and improve understanding and knowledge of the potential environmental impacts and benefits of offshore windfarm developments in UK waters'*.

Collaboration is key

The unique collaborative nature of COWRIE is recognised within the acronym itself and came about during an early meeting between The Crown Estate, British Wind Energy Association (BWEA) (now RenewableUK) and the Department of Trade and Industry (the forerunner to BERR and DECC) to discuss the proposed programme of work. All new entities require a name, identity or brand, so attempts were made to come up with a name that embraced the collaborative nature of the new organisation while maintaining a 'marine'

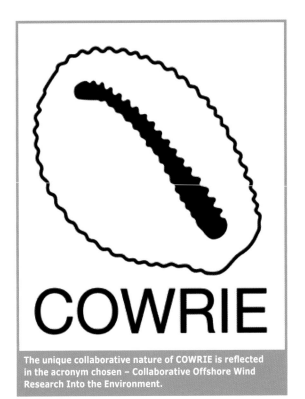

The unique collaborative nature of COWRIE is reflected in the acronym chosen – Collaborative Offshore Wind Research Into the Environment.

focus. The name chosen, 'Collaborative Offshore Wind Research into the Environment', formed the acronym 'COWRIE' after a common marine shell. As COWRIE became more established, and acquired company and charitable status, it required a logo and brand. e-bloc Interactive was tasked with designing a logo and came up with the shell 'imprint' which is very recognisable and can be easily printed in a range of housestyles for letter heads, report covers, PowerPoint® slides, etc.

During the early days expectations were relatively modest due to COWRIE's anticipated short-term lifespan to support Round 1 and the limited funding (interest accrued on the refundable deposits paid by each developer awarded an Agreement for Lease on a 10 km^2 area of seabed). The offshore windfarm sector was a new marine industry, so it made sense that the first round of projects were intended to act as demonstrations providing opportunities for developers, regulators, conservation bodies and other marine users to work together to learn more about the technical, economic and environmental constraints of developing offshore. If COWRIE was able to bring together expertise from these bodies and the developers in a constructive forum to agree a research programme that could deliver practical outputs in the short term for the benefit of the industry, then its goals had been met. At that stage it was not envisaged that COWRIE would gather momentum over the next decade to become a recognised model for collaborative research and a provider of industry best practice.

Meetings in those early days could be frustratingly long as the various parties had much to discuss to determine how best to allocate COWRIE's relatively modest amount of funding. The three key themes identified at that stage – impacts on birds, underwater noise and electromagnetic fields – were all issues that required significant research (including field studies), so each had the potential to require substantial funding. COWRIE had given itself a difficult task to ensure that the funds available were used to maximise benefits in several research areas. It was only able to achieve this aspiration through widespread support from the many experts and organisations able to give freely of their time to COWRIE, thereby minimising administrative costs. Even as COWRIE closes, an important measure of its success is evident in the number of individuals and organisations who have contributed to its work programme over the years and have given time to attend meetings, agree priority research topics, prepare scopes of work and tender specifications, assess tender bids, comment on draft reports, contribute to a peer review process and promote the work of COWRIE at all opportunities. It would appear that all those people have enjoyed contributing to COWRIE and are pleased to have been instrumental to its success.

Education and communications strategy

When COWRIE expanded through the Round 2 offshore windfarm programme, a small dedicated Education and Communications Working Group (ECWG) was formed to advance the key COWRIE objective of *'raising awareness of the UK offshore windfarm programme through a comprehensive education, communications and outreach strategy'*. This has been achieved in a number of ways:

- publication of COWRIE funded reports, guidance and survey results through the COWRIE website;
- use of the COWRIE website to provide access to the COWRIE Data Management System;
- interactive resources (windfarm map and COWRIE timeline);
- a poster summarising COWRIE's research themes against a backdrop of a map of the UK offshore windfarm programme;
- development of online teaching resources;

- running schools workshops;
- annual COWRIE Student Awards;
- dedicated stakeholder events;
- conference presentations.

To ensure the widest possible dissemination of its activities (including tender opportunities, published research studies and guidance), COWRIE set up a dedicated website – initially as a section of The Crown Estate's website but from 2006 through an independent, authoritative information portal with its own domain name, www.offshorewind.co.uk.

COWRIE research reports

Ensuring access to COWRIE research findings is the most fundamental aspect of COWRIE's education and communication work. Published reports are the main vehicle by which the findings of COWRIE-sponsored research studies are made available to interested parties. To ensure readability and consistency of branding, all reports are produced in a standard COWRIE-style format.

Being of a very technical nature the reports are aimed mainly at those with direct involvement in the industry such as

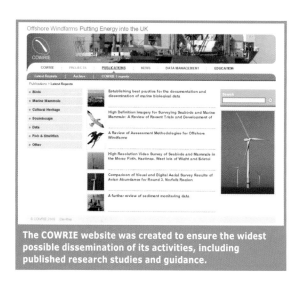

The COWRIE website was created to ensure the widest possible dissemination of its activities, including published research studies and guidance.

government advisors, developers, environmental consultants preparing environmental impact assessments (EIAs), non-governmental organisations (NGOs), researchers and specialist marine interest groups. All reports are accompanied by a non-technical summary, making the key findings of the studies available to a wider general public.

All reports are made available in downloadable electronic format online and some have also been printed in hard copy to ensure they are accessible to a wider audience. For example, the archaeological reports have become a 'mini-series' in their own right, published in a similar style and containing many illustrations which help bring the guidance 'to life.' Each report has an ISBN number to ensure traceability and copies are deposited with the British Library to ensure they are accessible in the public domain, are archived, and therefore will be available beyond the life of COWRIE.

All the reports have been subject to peer review prior to publication. This activity was performed mainly by specialist members of the COWRIE working group that commissioned the work, although some more specialist reports have been subjected to a full external peer review by international experts in that field of research. The reviewers have been given the opportunity to comment on both interim and final drafts.

COWRIE website – www.offshorewind.co.uk

The ECWG's first priority was the design, development and release of COWRIE's website. The site was first launched in 2006 and relaunched in 2008 with revised content and a new, easy-to-navigate layout. Website design and maintenance have been carried out by e-bloc Interactive.

The website serves as the external face of COWRIE to raise public and industry awareness of its research and data management activities, to facilitate dialogue with interested organisations, and to increase public awareness and understanding of the offshore wind industry and the environmental issues that surround it. It includes:

- information on the context and development of the UK offshore windfarm programme to date;
- an explanation of the role played by different government departments and interested parties;

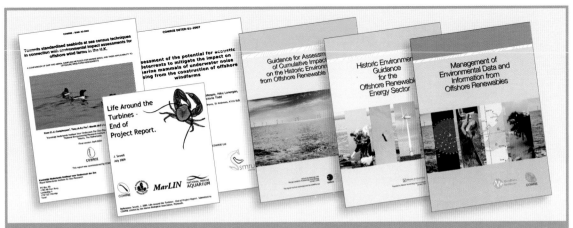

COWRIE research reports are aimed primarily at those with a direct involvement in the offshore wind energy industry. All reports are accompanied by a non-technical summary, making the key findings accessible to the wider public.

- information about UK offshore windfarm projects;
- a signposted link to COWRIE's Data Management System – the repository for the environmental data collected by developers as part of their environmental impact assessments (EIAs) and post-construction and operation monitoring activities.

In addition to the COWRIE commissioned reports, other sections of the website include information on stakeholder events held, workshops and conferences attended, a list of useful links and a number of interactive and educational resources for schools. It also provided a vehicle for publicising COWRIE news updates, new tender opportunities and interim reports on research projects in progress.

Visitors to the website were able to register for email updates whenever tender opportunities or new reports were published. They could also sign-up to receive the COWRIE e-newsletter, which was produced on a regular basis in the early years to keep readers up-to-date on COWRIE news, project developments, and attendance at conferences and seminars.

To assess its usefulness, traffic through the COWRIE website was monitored regularly by e-bloc Interactive from March 2009 using Google Analytics. From these statistics it has been possible to assess access to the site. Some of the most commonly viewed pages include Publications, Projects (information on projects underway) and the COWRIE interactive windfarm map.

The level of traffic through the website has highlighted its success in meeting COWRIE's education and communications objectives. For example, from March to October 2009, there was an average of 3,400 visitors per month to the website of which 2,840 were unique visits. The data show the website receives an average of 51 real visits per day. The majority of users (68%) are from the UK, though the website has been visited regularly by users from at least 81 different countries, especially users in the USA, Germany, the Netherlands, Spain, France and Canada – emphasising the significance of COWRIE's research to the global industry. Visits to the website increased markedly when a new report was published.

The COWRIE website is seen as an important source for information and a number of other organisations maintain links to it on their websites.

Once COWRIE is disbanded in 2010, the website will be refreshed and then maintained

www.offshorewind.co.uk, launched in 2006, is the external face of COWRIE.

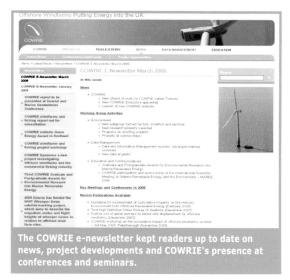

The COWRIE e-newsletter kept readers up to date on news, project developments and COWRIE's presence at conferences and seminars.

for several years to come so that all the reports and guidance documents are still accessible to all. The website will thus provide a COWRIE research archive along with an interactive version of the new poster (see below).

It is hoped the website will continue to serve as an important information resource, providing details of research undertaken and online resources, and serving as a repository and archive for all COWRIE research reports for several years to come. The online education resources will also be made available by MarLIN (The Marine Life Information Network – www.marlin.ac.uk) which intends to further develop additional resources if possible.

The COWRIE Data Management System has already been transferred to The Crown Estate which will incorporate the data into its own MaRS data and GIS product (see www.thecrownestate.co.uk).

Interactive resources

COWRIE web resources include an interactive map and timeline designed to provide basic information about the development of the UK offshore windfarm sector.

The Interactive Map pinpoints the locations of UK windfarm developments (Rounds 1 and 2)

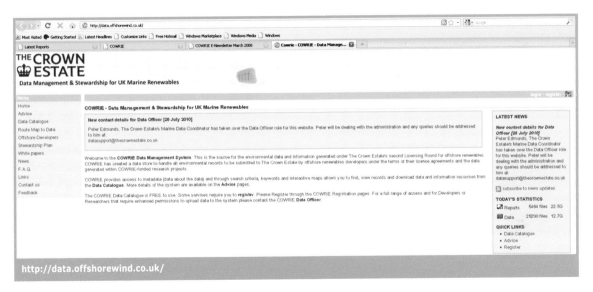

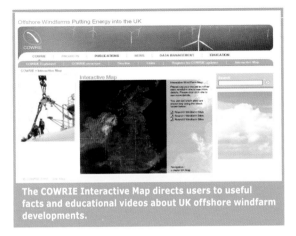

The COWRIE Interactive Map directs users to useful facts and educational videos about UK offshore windfarm developments.

The interactive timeline provides a visual representation of COWRIE's journey, from its establishment in 2001.

and makes use of Flash® technology to direct users to useful facts and educational videos about each location. Users of the interactive map can rollover the windfarm locations to find out the site name, owner and geographic co-ordinates, as well as useful facts relating to each project. By clicking on the map, users enter a three-dimensional Flash animation of an offshore windfarm, where they can click on 'hotspots' to access short video clips with accompanying narrated information.

The interactive timeline provides a visual sequence and timing of past and future COWRIE events along with key milestones in the development of the UK offshore windfarm programme. Each 'stop' on the timeline is accompanied by an image; the journey begins in 2001 when COWRIE was established and takes in key milestones in the development of the UK offshore wind industry. For example we learn that on 30 July 2005 the Kentish Flats offshore windfarm was commissioned and began to generate electricity. In December 2005, COWRIE received charitable status. Most recently, in September 2010, a major milestone was reached with the opening of Thanet offshore windfarm, which took the UK renewables sector beyond 5 GW of installed capacity (combined onshore and offshore).

Poster

To mark the closure of COWRIE and in addition to this book, an A3 size poster was published in June 2010 to promote the key achievements of the COWRIE programme. The large-scale format provides a simple, concise and attractive presentation of each research theme against the backdrop of a UK offshore windfarm map. It is ideal for display in a classroom or office environment.

The poster aims to convey, on one sheet, a summary of COWRIE, its activities and deliverables between 2001 and 2010. A number of text boxes provide an explanation of COWRIE governance and research themes set against a map of Britain showing the location of Round 1, 2 and 3 offshore windfarm projects and leased areas, along with information on the owner/operator.

The poster acts as a snapshot and signpost, directing the reader to find out more about COWRIE from its website. Adopting the same thematic format and colour coding as this book, the poster provides a snapshot of the range of research projects under COWRIE, split into the following categories:

- marine data and management;
- education and communication;
- coastal processes;
- birds;

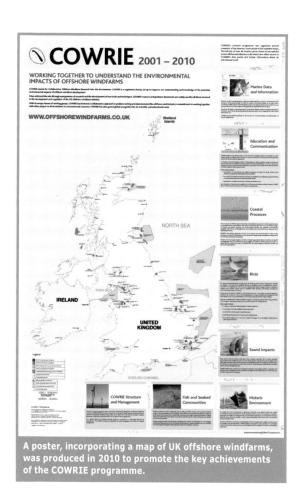

A poster, incorporating a map of UK offshore windfarms, was produced in 2010 to promote the key achievements of the COWRIE programme.

- sound impacts;
- historic environment;
- fish and seabed communities.

The poster also directs readers to the COWRIE website where they will find an enhanced version of the Interactive Map (using Google® mapping technology and designed by La Tene Maps) and timeline with links to the offshore projects and other relevant information. Given the increased attention being given to UK offshore windfarm development through Government policy, it is anticipated that the poster and Interactive Map will be of great interest in the future as an informal and formal educational tool.

'Life Around the Turbines'

COWRIE's 'Life Around the Turbines' project was proposed by the ECWG in response to the increased demand for dedicated curriculum-based educational resources aimed at the schools market. The project consisted of two elements – workshops for primary school children and online educational resources available for free download from the COWRIE website.

The project was led by MarLIN (The Marine Life Information Network) and its specialist educators at the Marine Biological Association (MBA), with assistance from staff at the National Marine Aquarium. e-bloc Interactive

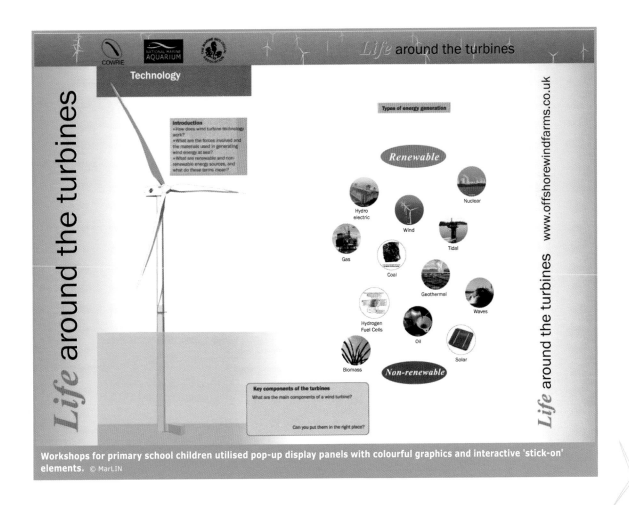

Workshops for primary school children utilised pop-up display panels with colourful graphics and interactive 'stick-on' elements. © MarLIN

provided additional web support. The initiative was run in two main phases – between October 2008 and April 2009, and between January and July 2010.

During the first phase of the project, workshops and online educational resources were designed for English National Curriculum Key Stage 2 and linked to subjects including science, design technology and citizenship. The project focused on the following educational themes:

- **Habitats, adaptation and food webs:** exploring the species and habitats found around windfarms and how these species are connected by the food web.
- **Wind turbines and the environment:** examining the planning process associated with responsible windfarm development and the different issues that need to be addressed before a development can take place.

- **How turbines work:** learning about the workings of a wind turbine and the need for renewable energy.

During the second phase, all educational resources were also linked to the Scottish and Welsh National Curriculums and educational resources were developed for two additional themes:

- **Undersea noise:** a lesson exploring how sound travels underwater, how marine animals use sound, how they may be affected by noise associated with windfarms and how this might be mitigated. The lesson includes games and activities using sound.
- **Keeping the turbines standing:** an interactive practical activity where pupils are asked to design structures to maintain wind turbines in water tanks using a

Over 200 primary school students in years 4–6 attended the first round of COWRIE schools workshops. © MarLIN

selection of materials. This is linked to the design process behind offshore wind turbine development.

Workshops for primary school children

During the first phase of 'Life Around the Turbines', workshops were held for primary school children in two locations. Two one-day workshops were held at the National Marine Aquarium, Plymouth, attended by 115 pupils from two different schools, and a workshop was held at the Orbis Energy Centre, Lowestoft, attended by 101 pupils from two different schools. The workshops were free to participating schools and targeted children in years 4, 5 and 6 (ages 8–11). Participating schools were local to the workshop venues and coach transportation was provided where schools were not within walking distance.

Each day-long workshop consisted of a carousel of three different activities, each lasting an hour and corresponding to the three educational themes:

- habitats, adaptation and food webs;
- wind turbines and the environment;
- how turbines work.

Pencils, bookmarks and badges were distributed to pupils and teachers attending the workshops.
© MarLIN

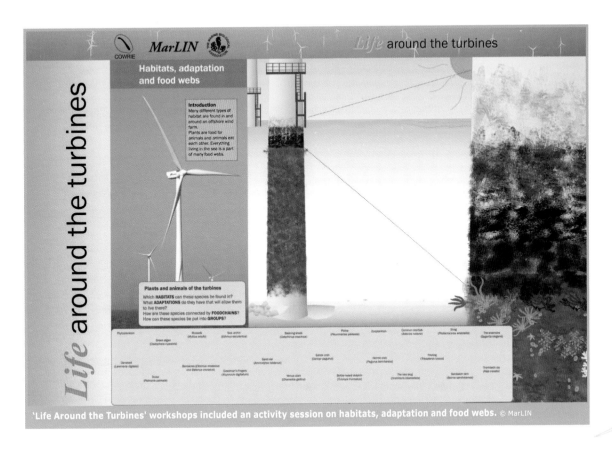

'Life Around the Turbines' workshops included an activity session on habitats, adaptation and food webs. © MarLIN

Activities were led by staff from MBA and the National Marine Aquarium. For each activity, pop-up display panels were produced with colourful graphics and interactive 'stick-on' elements. These interactive display panels provided a backdrop and prompt material for the activities and were designed to be reused and usable in any location, providing flexibility as to the location of future workshops. Pencils, bookmarks and badges were produced for distribution at the workshops to promote the COWRIE website and online educational resources to students and teachers.

During the second phase of 'Life Around the Turbines', the programme of primary school workshops was extended around the country, with two days of workshops held at eight locations (Bideford, Bridlington, Brighton, Edinburgh, Llandudno, Lowestoft, Pembrokeshire and Swanage) selected for their importance to the future development of offshore wind. A total of 822 children attended the second phase of workshops.

Teachers and participating pupils were asked to provide feedback after all workshops. Feedback was extremely positive. In response to the question 'If there was anything you could change about the workshops, what would it be?' many children stated that they wouldn't change anything and others wanted more workshops, a longer day or more activities. Teachers also provided extremely positive verbal feedback and many expressed an interest in returning should the workshops be repeated in the future. Unfortunately several schools that had expressed interest were unable to attend the second phase of workshops, which was filled to capacity indicating the high level of interest in educational resources of this kind.

In the words of one teacher, whose class attended one of the Phase 1 workshops:

"Thanks for a really fantastic day. The kids really had a blast and learnt so much. It was pitched just right and active and exciting. It really finished off our topic and helped us think about what we could do next year when we do it again."

Full reports on both phases of the workshops are available from the Education pages of the COWRIE website.

Online educational resources

A range of web resources aimed at children and teachers was developed to complement and supplement the workshops provided for primary school children. These are available for all to use on the Education pages of the COWRIE website, with teaching resources also made available on the MarLIN website.

'Life Around the Turbines' is a Flash-based, interactive seabed where visitors can explore the marine habitats found around an offshore windfarm. Users can visit 10 different habitat zones ranging from 'In the air and on the water' to 'Scour defence' and 'On the monopile,' rolling over the habitat graphics with their mouse to find out about the species that live there.

The Education section of the COWRIE website also directs users to information about more than 60 marine species that may be encountered around offshore windfarms in UK waters.

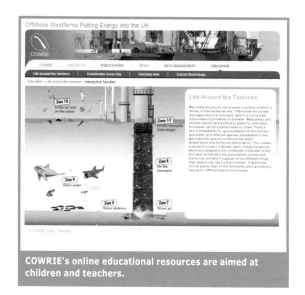

COWRIE's online educational resources are aimed at children and teachers.

Online teaching resources are provided for five themes:
- habitats, adaptation and food webs;
- wind turbines and the environment;
- how turbines work;
- undersea noise;
- keeping the turbines standing.

Resources were developed for English National Curriculum Key Stage 2 and have been adapted for the Scottish and Welsh National Curriculums. Resources include activity sheets, teachers' notes, instructions for classroom games and PowerPoint® versions of the display panels used for games during the primary school workshops.

It is hoped that these resources will enable information about windfarms to be taught in schools around the country.

In addition, the industry has highlighted a potential shortfall in the necessary skills that the offshore programme will demand and it is hoped that an extension of COWRIE's educational work to secondary level,

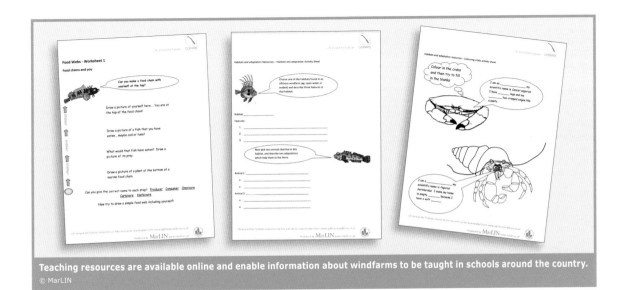

Teaching resources are available online and enable information about windfarms to be taught in schools around the country.
© MarLIN

Table 9.1 Winners of COWRIE Student Awards.		
Year	**Title**	**Level**
2007	Offshore windfarms and commercial fisheries: a focused desk study of the Greater Wash area of the southern North Sea – Duncan Ayling, Cranfield University	MSc
	The Evopod marine current turbine – David Mohamad, University of Newcastle	MSc
2008	The potential impact of magnetic fields emitted from the UK's first offshore windfarm sub-sea cables on the behaviour of the shore crab (*Carcinus maenas*) – Nicola Everitt, University of Newcastle	MSc
	The transverse horizontal axis water turbine – Ross McAdam, University of Oxford	Undergraduate
	Passive pitching control of oscillating hydrofoils – David Ferguson, University of Strathclyde	Undergraduate
2009	A wave energy converter software module for the Simulating WAves nearshore (SWAN) wave modelling package – Charles Pearce, University of Exeter	Undergraduate
	Marine current turbines: array effects – Miguel Gallego Gómez, University of Strathclyde	MSc

emphasising the engineering and technical opportunities as well as the environmental, will encourage more students to pursue a career in the marine renewables sector.

COWRIE Student Awards

The annual COWRIE Student Awards scheme was set up in 2006 in recognition of the increasing attention paid to the marine renewables industry in undergraduate and postgraduate programmes and to further encourage students to pursue a career within the offshore renewables sector (the scheme was not limited to the offshore wind sector).

The award scheme consisted of two categories – best undergraduate thesis and best Masters project. Winners received a prize of £750 and were given the opportunity to present their project at a BWEA conference or another COWRIE event. Nominations were submitted by tutors at UK universities and the shortlisted projects were assessed by a selection panel drawn from members of the COWRIE Board and the Education and Communications Working Group. Table 9.1 lists the winning projects.

Stakeholder events

Reaching out to and communicating with stakeholders in offshore wind energy development has consistently been an important part of COWRIE's work. Although the website was the main point of contact for information, COWRIE recognised the need for more direct contact with interest groups. This was achieved through sponsored events designed to gain access to, and bring together, particular stakeholder groups and to encourage discussion between the multiple stakeholders in offshore wind energy developments.

COWRIE has arranged visits to offshore projects to enable stakeholders to learn more

about the industry. These proved increasingly popular as the majority of stakeholders have very limited opportunities to get out to an operating windfarm with the owner/operator explaining the key processes in its development and construction. The feedback from these visits was extremely positive as participants found that they came away much better informed and having enjoyed the opportunity to discuss common issues in a constructive setting.

In addition to 'days at sea', COWRIE has facilitated many conventional meetings to discuss common issues.

Boat trips

On 30 November 2008 COWRIE held its first boat trip for stakeholders, travelling from Gravesend Pier to the Kentish Flats windfarm (owned and operated by Vattenfall). There were presentations on board from representatives of COWRIE, BWEA (now RenewableUK) and the windfarm, with time for discussion and networking. The day was an opportunity for stakeholders from a diverse range of organisations to debate planning and consenting issues in the context of a working windfarm and generated much positive feedback. Discussion centred on the engineering and logistical difficulties of building and operating a windfarm at sea, as well as consenting and environmental issues. Short video interviews ('vox pops') were conducted with selected attendees and posted on the COWRIE website. The day was attended by representatives from COWRIE, BWEA, Government departments and agencies (including DECC, Defra, Department for Transport, Marine and Fisheries Agency, Natural England, Maritime and Coastguard Agency, Cefas), local councils, marine wildlife groups and academia.

Building on the success of this event and the positive feedback, it was decided to run further boat trips around the country in 2010. For this second round of events the priorities were to extend the reach of the events by running boat trips in a number of different locations and to attract a diverse range of stakeholders with a local interest in the development of offshore wind. To this end, COWRIE liaised with local Coastal Partnerships around the country to advertise the boat trips to a wide variety of marine stakeholders; participating Coastal Partnerships issued invitations to their members and attendees included local councillors, ecologists, representatives of regional development agencies and staff from the local offices of national organisations such as Natural England and RSPB.

A stakeholder visit to the Burbo Bank windfarm (owned and operated by Dong Energy) was held on 25 May 2010, departing from Liverpool on board a Mersey ferry. The event was attended by a large number of marine and offshore wind stakeholders from northwest England with presentations from COWRIE, RenewableUK and Dong Energy.

On 8 June 2010 there was a stakeholder event for the east of England, with presentations and discussion at an onshore facility in Great Yarmouth followed by a boat trip to the Scroby Sands windfarm (owned and operated by E.ON) in the afternoon. The presentations and opportunity to address questions to the Scroby Sands production engineer provided a valuable opportunity to clear up many local misconceptions surrounding the operation of the windfarm.

A final stakeholder boat trip is planned for October 2010 at the recently opened Gunfleet Sands windfarm (owned and operated by Dong Energy). Marine stakeholders from southeast England will be given the opportunity to hear presentations from COWRIE, RenewableUK and Dong Energy while on board a vessel steaming out of Clacton, before being treated to a close-up view of their local offshore windfarm.

In addition to these COWRIE-run events, sponsorship was provided for an RSPB marine stakeholder boat trip in the Firth of Forth (June 2010). This was a valuable opportunity for

COWRIE has arranged visits to offshore windfarms to enable stakeholders to learn more about the industry. © Philip Ward

offshore wind and other marine stakeholders to discuss common issues relating to the environmentally sustainable development of this economically important area. This trip offered a key opportunity for COWRIE to contribute to the development of stakeholder relations in Scotland and we are grateful to RSPB for organising the event.

'Sharing the Sea', March 2007

In March 2007 COWRIE sponsored a BWEA-facilitated meeting for marine stakeholders called 'Sharing the Sea.' This was held just before the BWEA's 4th Annual Wave and Tidal Energy Conference and consisted of presentations with opportunities for discussion and the prioritisation of actions to reduce uncertainties surrounding the deployment of offshore energy devices. There were sessions on 'Navigation, Recreation and Maritime Safety' and 'The UK Marine Environment' with speakers from maritime agencies and conservation bodies.

Conferences and outreach events

COWRIE has maintained a regular programme of outreach work participating in conferences, seminars and meetings at the local, national and international level. Various members of the Board and Technical Working Groups have made presentations at these events on behalf of COWRIE.

BWEA (now RenewableUK) conferences

COWRIE attended the BWEA annual conference from 2005 to 2010. This provided an opportunity to raise awareness of COWRIE among developers and researchers, and to contribute to discussions surrounding the environmental impacts of offshore wind energy developments.

- **BWEA27, Cardiff, 2005.** COWRIE sponsored its first environmental research seminar entitled 'Generic Research into the Environmental Impacts of Offshore Wind Energy Developments'. The seminar was an opportunity to introduce COWRIE's work – including the launch of its website and the Data Management Information Plan for Marine Renewables – and to provide updates on ongoing COWRIE research projects. Invited external speakers gave presentations on the government's role in offshore windfarm research and research into navigation risks and their assessment.
- **BWEA28, Glasgow, 2006.** COWRIE again sponsored an environmental research seminar. This included an update on COWRIE's work to date, presentation of COWRIE research findings and an update on the work of the UK government's Research Advisory Group (RAG) for offshore wind.
- **BWEA29, Glasgow, 2007.** At this event COWRIE introduced the first Student Award

COWRIE Board member, Dr Carolyn Heeps, chaired the Project Development and Consenting Session at RenewableUK's Offshore Wind 2010 Conference.
© RenewableUK

winners who presented their projects. The conference was also used to launch COWRIE's new guidance on 'Management of Environmental Data and Information from Offshore Renewables' and the new COWRIE data management website. Live demonstrations of the new Data Management System were given at the COWRIE exhibition stand and received many visitors.

- **BWEA30, London, 2008.** Updates on ongoing COWRIE research projects were presented at a short COWRIE session and the winners of the second annual COWRIE Student Awards presented posters on their winning projects.
- **BWEA31, Liverpool, 2009.** With news of COWRIE funding coming to an end, this event provided an opportunity to explain the COWRIE legacy including a developer's perspective entitled 'What has COWRIE ever done for us?'
- BWEA became RenewableUK in March 2010 and COWRIE attended **RenewableUK Offshore Wind 2010** in Liverpool in June as its final dedicated offshore event. COWRIE chaired the Project Development and Consenting session. Panel members participated in a lively debate centred on the proposed new consenting regime for large-scale offshore wind development. The COWRIE input highlighted how the offshore industry (with the aid of COWRIE initiatives) had demonstrated its commitment to finding practical solutions to de-risking development at an early stage through robust Environmental Statements and appropriate mitigation measures.

Other UK events

COWRIE was a sponsor of the 2007 Coastal Futures Conference 'Adaptive Management & Offshore Wind Energy' organised by CMS (Coastal Management for Sustainability). The conference assessed current understanding of the environmental impact and benefits of offshore wind to pose the question of whether environmental impact assessment (EIA), strategic environment assessment (SEA) and monitoring practice could be revised in the light of existing knowledge. COWRIE gave a joint presentation with JNCC on the research agenda and remaining issues to be covered.

In collaboration with BERR, COWRIE was a lead sponsor of MAREE 2008, the International Scientific Meeting on Marine Renewable Energy and the Environment held in London in June 2008. This international conference aimed to:

- distil the evidence base on the environmental effects of marine renewable energy developments;
- define the major basic and applied environmental research questions that remain to be answered for strategic and project level environmental management;
- facilitate information exchange between scientists, regulators and industry.

Other events included a presentation at the Local Government Association's Coastal Special Interest Group Annual Conference in Whitstable in June 2009.

Overseas events

As well as regular participation in UK events, COWRIE has been represented at meetings and conferences in Europe and the USA to raise awareness of its work at the international level. COWRIE representatives have participated in:

- a French workshop on offshore wind held in Le Havre in 2006;
- a Danish conference held in 2006 to launch the five-year monitoring review of the Nysted and Horns Rev windfarms;
- the European Policy Workshop on Offshore Wind Power Deployment held in Berlin in 2007;
- a conference at the Roger Williams School of Law, Rhode Island, USA in 2008.

Members have also taken the opportunity to promote COWRIE's work during visits to the UK by a number of international delegations.

Scottish Green Energy Awards 2009

COWRIE was named Best Environmental Initiative at the prestigious 2009 Scottish Renewables Green Energy Awards. The award, sponsored by BRE Scotland, recognises how the renewables industry, projects and/or initiatives can assist in achieving wider environmental goals. COWRIE was selected from a shortlist of four initiatives, all of which represented significant contributions to the renewables industry in Scotland.

The award was presented at a prestigious dinner for 600 guests held in Edinburgh in December 2009 and was accepted on behalf of COWRIE by Trustee and Board member, Dr Carolyn Heeps, who said:

"I am accepting this Award on behalf of the many people that have contributed to the research and studies that COWRIE has

Board member Dr Carolyn Heeps accepts the award for Best Environmental Initiative at the 2009 Scottish Renewables Green Energy Awards on behalf of COWRIE.
© Rob McDougall

conducted since it was established in 2001. In particular, the offshore wind sector has made a significant contribution to the development of best practice, demonstrating that it takes its environmental responsibilities very seriously."

COWRIE was nominated for this award on the basis that, as a charity independent of government, it demonstrated a unique ability to bring together key industry players to help shape research requirements and to develop best practice guidance for the offshore wind sector. The Award recognised the contribution of all those who have participated in COWRIE's programme of activities and is a fitting acknowledgement of their commitment and dedication.

The COWRIE legacy

COWRIE has provided the industry with the necessary platform to become involved in developing and disseminating best practice and, in this way, has promoted sustainable development practices and decision-making based on strong and improved scientific understanding. COWRIE has made all its research findings publically available on its website, which has gained an international reputation as a source of authoritative scientific publications with practical applications for industry.

A number of final events and initiatives are planned to coincide with the ending of COWRIE in late 2010. These 'legacy events' are a way to ensure that the work of COWRIE – in particular the large research output and best practice guidance – remains in the public consciousness and continues to add value to the further development of offshore wind energy in the future. The events will also serve to recognise and applaud the enormous voluntary contribution made to COWRIE by individuals from a number of sectors and organisations without whom the work of COWRIE would not have been possible.

Key events planned include:

- a stand at the RenewableUK annual conference in Glasgow on 2–4 November 2010 to launch this book and the refreshed version of the website;
- more workshops for schools, with an emphasis on new materials for secondary education;
- additional stakeholder visits to operating offshore windfarms including a dedicated visit for environmental journalists. These visits will enable a broader range of stakeholders than ever to visit and have the opportunity to learn about offshore wind development in the UK and air their views.

Through its comprehensive programme of research COWRIE has helped all of us to obtain a better understanding of the impacts of offshore wind development. Using this new knowledge, developers can build and operate their projects in a responsible and environmentally friendly way. We can all benefit from the positive aspects of renewable energy whilst knowing that the environment is not being harmed. But as we enter this major step change towards the large-scale 'industrialisation' of the offshore wind energy programme in the UK, there is a realisation that new environmental challenges face us within the sector and the way we work alongside other marine industries. Large-scale projects, much further offshore and in deeper water, in areas where there are significant gaps in our data and understanding – combined with the likely requirement for new approaches and methodologies for survey design, data collection, analysis and

Thanet offshore windfarm became operational in September 2010. Its 100 turbines have a combined capacity of 300 MW.
© Jamie Cook, Vattenfall

interpretation – mean that additional research is required.

The move from site-specific environmental assessment to Zone-wide assessment (which has greater similarities to regional environmental assessment) will bring with it new questions and novel solutions. The Crown Estate's delivery programme for Round 3 will see it working closely with Zone developers and establishing specialist groups to tackle key issues during the development and consenting phases. Developers with projects in Scottish territorial waters have already shown that a more collaborative approach to some surveys and studies can work and is able to address cumulative and in-combination issues.

Despite its initial 'growing pains' COWRIE has been recognised for providing a platform for industry players to develop excellent working relationships – not only with each other, but also with key stakeholders and interest groups. COWRIE has engaged with, and drawn upon, the expertise of the most knowledgeable academics, research scientists and consultants in the fields of ornithology, underwater noise, marine mammal studies, fish behaviour, marine heritage and coastal processes.

On this basis the UK offshore wind energy industry has demonstrated that it is an industry that not only believes in sustainable development, but is also willing to identify issues of concern with stakeholders and to address those concerns through well-developed research programmes and the implementation of best practice. The outputs from COWRIE have not always been wholly conclusive and have generated considerable debate, but they have also provided a firmer basis on which to go forward. Most importantly, the experience has shown that it is important to bring together interested parties in a constructive forum and environment to work collaboratively on key issues of concern.

We believe that this is the true legacy of COWRIE.

Annex 1. Technical Working Groups

The Technical Working Groups consist of invited experts and developer representatives and are chaired by a trustee. These Groups have evolved and changed in size as different specialists joined to assist with different studies.

The first three Technical Working Groups were set up in 2005 when COWRIE became a charity. The fourth (Futures) was set up when The Crown Estate and the Government announced the start of Round 3.

Before 2005 those listed as COWRIE 1 Steering Group Members participated in all aspects of the COWRIE 1 work programme. Since that time several individuals have moved to other organisations but retained their participation in the various working groups.

Some individuals contributed to the work of COWRIE without being members of a specific group and are listed under 'Other Contributors'.

Environment Technical Working Group

Richard Mellish, Chair and Trustee
Duncan Ayling, RenewableUK (formerly BWEA)
Ben Barton, The Crown Estate
Craig Bloomer, Joint Nature Conservation Committee (JNCC)
Philip Bloor, Department of Energy and Climate Change (DECC)
Louise Burton, Natural England
Victoria Copley, Natural England
Zoe Crutchfield, JNCC then Mainstream Renewable Power (industry representative)
Alexandra Georgescu, DECC
John Hartley, Hartley Anderson Consultants
Chris Hill, GeoData Institute
Jesper Krarup Holst, DONG Energy (industry representative)

Adrian Judd, Centre for Environment, Fisheries & Aquaculture Science (Cefas)
Rowena Langston, The Royal Society for the Protection of Birds (RSPB)
Jonathan Lartice, Department for Environment, Food and Rural Affairs (Defra)
Peter Madigan, RenewableUK (formerly BWEA)
Sonia Mendes, JNCC
Rachael Mills, Marine Management Organisation (MMO) – formerly Marine and Fisheries Agency (MFA)
Shaun Nicholson, MMO (formerly MFA)
Christopher Pater, English Heritage
Andrew Prior, JNCC then PMSS (consultants)
Jamie Rendell, Defra
Frank Thomsen, Cefas
Paul Townsend, Maritime and Coast Guard Agency (MCGA)
Gero Vella, RES Offshore (industry representative)
Angela Wratten, DECC
Michael Young, Natural England.

Data Technical Working Group

Carolyn Heeps, Chair and Trustee
Ben Barton, The Crown Estate
Bill Cooper, ABPmer Limited
Charmaine Govindasamy, Defra
Chris Hill, GeoData Institute
Carla Houghton, RWE npower (industry representative)
Stephen King, Hartley Anderson Consultants
Peter Madigan, RenewableUK (formerly BWEA)
David McArthur, independent consultant
Rachael Mills, MMO (formerly MFA)
Shaun Nicholson, MMO (formerly MFA)
Jon Parr, Marine Biological Association (MBA)
Jason Sadler, GeoData Institute
Harvey Tyler-Walters, MBA
Angela Wratten, DECC.

Education and Communications Working Group

This working group is composed of all five trustees (see Annex 2):
David Still (chairman)
Rob Hastings
Carolyn Heeps
Richard Mellish
Alan Moore.

Futures Working Group

David Still, Chair and Trustee
Philip Bloor, DECC
John Hartley, Hartley Anderson Consultants
Carolyn Heeps, The Crown Estate and then
    Fred Olsen Renewables
Chris Hill, GeoData Institute
Cathryn Hooper, Mainstream Renewable Power
    (industry representative)
Danielle Lane, The Crown Estate
Peter Madigan, RenewableUK (formerly BWEA)
Tim Norman, The Crown Estate.

Birds Subgroup

Sarah Anthony, Natural England
Craig Bloomer, JNCC
Philip Bloor, DECC
Louise Burton, Natural England
Victoria Copley, Natural England
Zoe Crutchfield, JNCC then Mainstream
    Renewables Power (industry representative)
Allan Drewitt, Natural England
Alexandra Fawcett, Natural England
John Hartley, Hartley Anderson Consultants
Sue King, AMEC (consultants)
Rowena Langston, RSPB
Tim Norman, The Crown Estate
Sue O'Brien, JNCC
Andrew Prior, JNCC then PMSS (consultants)

Gero Vella, RES Offshore (industry representative)
Sian Whitehead, Countryside Council for Wales
    (CCW)
Michael Young, Natural England.

Fish, Shellfish and Benthos Subgroup

Louise Burton, Natural England
Victoria Copley, Natural England
Jim Ellis, Cefas
Alexandra Fawcett, Natural England
Peter Hayes, Marine Scotland
Adrian Judd, Cefas
Mandy McMath, CCW
Rachael Mills, MMO (formerly MFA)
Derek Moore, Marine Scotland
Shaun Nicholson, MMO (formerly MFA)
Ian Reach, Natural England
Robert Thornhill, REW npower (industry
    representative)
Gero Vella, RES Offshore (industry
    representative)
Michael Young, Natural England.

Marine Mammals Subgroup

Philip Bloor, DECC
Louise Burton, Natural England
Victoria Copley, Natural England
Zoe Crutchfield, JNCC then Mainstream
    Renewable Power (industry representative)
John Hartley, Hartley Anderson Consultants
Jesper Krarup Holst, Dong Energy (industry
    representative)
Mandy McMath, CCW
Sonia Mendes, JNCC
Andrew Prior, JNCC then PMSS (consultants)
Kirsten Ramsay, CCW
Frank Thomsen, Cefas
Gero Vella, RES Offshore (industry representative)
Michael Young, Natural England.

COWRIE 1 Steering Group Members

Carolyn Heeps, The Crown Estate (Chairman)

Mike Brook, Department of Trade and Industry (DTI)

Victoria Copley, English Nature

Zoe Crutchfield, JNCC

Sandy Downie, Scottish Natural Heritage (SNH)

Julie Drew, AMEC (consultants)

Gordon Edge, BWEA (now RenewableUK)

David Farrier, Powergen

Frances Franklin, Cefas

Paul Gilliland, English Nature

James Glennie, BWEA (now RenewableUK)

Nick Goodall, BWEA (now RenewableUK)

Jacqueline Gray, The Crown Estate

Jim Halliday, Offshore Wind Energy Network (OWEN)

Alison Hill, BWEA (now RenewableUK)

Maggie Hill, CCW

Cathryn Hooper, The Crown Estate

Adrian Judd, Cefas

Rowena Langston, RSPB

Paul Leonard, Defra

Gareth Lewis, AMEC (consultants)

Georgia Markwell, RWE npower (industry representative)

Ashley Murray, English Nature

Kevin O'Carroll, DTI

Andrew Prior, JNCC

Gary Shanahan, DTI

Mark Tasker, JNCC

Simon Tribe, West Coast Energy (industry representative)

Gero Vella, RES Offshore (industry representative)

Sarah Wood, CCW.

Other Contributors

Rosemary Bradley, Department of Environment Northern Ireland

Bruna Catena, The Crown Estate

Dominic Counsell, Scottish Government

Simon Gooder, Marine and Coastal Guard Agency (MCGA)

Lynn Griffiths, Welsh Assembly Government

Michael Hay, RenewableUK (formerly BWEA)

Quentin Huggett, Geotek (industry representative)

George Lees, Scottish Government

Lorelei Line, E.ON (industry representative)

Sally Marine, Geotek (industry representative)

Jacky Martel, Natural England

Neal Rafferty, Scottish Government

Ralph Thornton, (industry representative).

Annex 2. COWRIE Board members – past and present

Alan Moore, Chairman COWRIE; Chairman of the industry-side of DECC's Renewables Advisory Board (RAB); Director of the Ventus Funds; Director of Partnerships for Renewables Ltd

Dr Carolyn Heeps, Company Secretary, COWRIE; Offshore Projects Manager at Fred Olsen Renewables Limited

Robert Hastings, Director of the Marine Estate at The Crown Estate; Member of the Renewables Advisory Board (RAB)

Richard Mellish, Head of Finance Strategy and Business Planning at the Department of Energy and Climate Change (DECC)

David Still, Managing Director of Clipper Windpower Marine Europe Limited; Member of the Renewables Advisory Board (RAB)

Frank Parrish, Board member until July 2006; Former Head of the Marine Estate at The Crown Estate (retired end 2005).

Annex 3. Administration and programme management

COWRIE Limited is an independent company which was registered as a charity on 20 December 2005. To ensure good governance and adherence to regulatory requirements, the COWRIE Board of Trustees contracted independent service providers to deliver the programme of work, to provide the website and to undertake accounting and auditing.

NatureBureau Limited provided overall co-ordination, project management and communications across COWRIE. NatureBureau administered the tendering process for projects and thereafter the contracts for COWRIE research projects, ensuring that all projects were delivered to time and to budget. It also provided Secretariat services for the Board and Technical Working Groups. NatureBureau was responsible for the dissemination of information and the content management of the website in close relation with the trustees and working groups and in line with COWRIE's charitable objectives.

The GeoData Institute developed, managed and implemented the Data Management and Information Plan.

e-bloc Interactive designed, established and hosted the COWRIE website.

JS2 Limited undertook financial management, control and accounting services.

Sayer Vincent (consultants and auditors) undertook the annual company audit.

COWRIE is particularly indebted to Dr Carolyn Heeps for all her efforts over the years as overall leader and director of the day-to-day programme management. Without her expertise, enthusiasm and encouragement COWRIE's achievements would have been considerably less.

The following people have contributed to the COWRIE work programme over the years:

NatureBureau Limited: Gemma Couzens, Chloe Delgery, Sarah Fowler, Tom Haynes, Eleanor Partridge, Brigitte Ruiz, Laurie Strike, Sue Thornton, Beki Vince; and the design team Barbara Creed, Peter Creed and Justine Pocock.

The GeoData Institute: Gemma Doneghan, Chris Hill, Jason Sadler.

e-bloc Interactive: Morgan Adams, Aaron Lowe.

JS2 Limited: Karey Banwell, John Speed. Sayer Vincent: Ian Barker, Vivien Ma, Helen Oakensen, Chibuzo Okpala, Kate Sayer, Neil Watters.